# Introduction

A 'Topic' is an approach to teaching in a Primary School which involves various apparently unrelated tasks being carried out under the umbrella of a common title or theme such as 'Vikings in Britain'.

Topic work always:

- includes class, group and individual work with some element of choice.
- involves practical activities.
- uses themes selected which are thought appropriate to the interests and stage of development of the children involved.
- involves first hand experiences such as a visit or visitors.
- involves some sort of investigation.
- involves information gathering skills.
- crosses some curriculum boundaries.

    It should also include, if possible, an element of *FUN*.

The purpose of this book is to provide a bank of ideas and photocopiable activities, based on the study of Viking Britain, which fulfil the above criteria. It is envisaged that a busy class teacher will use his or her professional judgement to select activities appropriate to their own individual situation.

Topical Resources publishes a range of Educational Materials for use in Primary Schools and Pre-School Nurseries and Playgroups.

**For latest catalogue:**

**Tel: 01772 863158**

**Fax: 01772 866153**

**E.Mail: sales@topical-resources.co.uk**

**For free sample pages, visit our website on:**

**www.topical-resources.co.uk**

Copyright © 2001 Paul Cross

Illustrated by John Hutchinson

Printed in Great Britain for 'Topical Resources', Publishes of Educational Materials, P.O. Box 329, Broughton, Preston. PR3 5LT by T. Snape & Company Ltd., Boltons Court, Preston.

Typeset by Artworks, 69 Worden Lane, Leyland, Lancashire. PR5 2BD Tel: 01772 431010

First Published May 2001
ISBN 1 872977 59 8

# Notes for Teachers

# Background Information for Class Lessons

## The Impact of the Vikings

The Vikings used to be portrayed in films and story books as merciless barbarians who ravaged, plundered and burnt their way across northern Europe from about 800 A.D. to about 1100 A.D. With their emblems of Thor's hammer and Odin's raven they came to stand for all that was evil, violent and destructive of anything civilised in Europe.

This view came from the writings of terrified monks and clerics whose abbeys, churches and monasteries in Britain were attacked from 793 onwards. They were reporting on the initial raids of the Norse men from across the seas. Simeon of Durham writing at the time states, "The harrying of the heathen miserably destroyed God's church on Lindisfarne. They laid waste with grievous plundering, trampled the holy places with polluted feet, dug up the altars and seized all the treasures of the holy church. They killed some of the brothers; some they took away with them in fetters; many they drove out, naked and loaded with insults; and some of them they drowned in the sea."

Such views of the Vikings persisted in people's concepts for centuries and are still part of the myths and legends surrounding them to this day. However modern archaeology, aided by scientific and literary studies have revealed a different picture. Emphasis now is placed on Viking trading rather than their raiding; their poetry and art rather than their pillaging; Viking technology rather than Viking terror. These dynamic and determined people from modern Denmark, Sweden and Norway had a far more positive effect, on the Britain they came to, for many different reasons. Vigorous new settlers opened up new areas of the country to farming. Their craftsmen brought new and inspiring art forms and their traders founded and developed new market towns. The Vikings brought new forms of administration to their towns and villages, new forms of justice and the very word, 'law' into the English language. The Viking voyages beyond Britain to Russia, Iceland, the Faroe Islands, Greenland and North America extended the civilised world's known boundaries. It appears the Vikings did everything with bravery, adventure and a robust courage.

## The Origins of the Viking

The very word 'Viking' is somewhat puzzling. An Old Norse word 'Vik' meant a bay or a creek, so Viking could have meant someone who keeps a ship in a bay, ready for fishing, trading or raiding. On the other hand an Old English word 'wic' borrowed from the Latin of the Romans meant a camp or trading place. So from the start the Vikings are given many differing roles. For centuries before the Vikings burst into Britain the inhabitants of modern day Scandinavia had been involved in trade with the north, east and the west. Furs from the north, ivory from the walruses of the deeply inset coasts, amber found on the Baltic coasts, speedy falcons from the wooded inland areas and human slaves captured in raids on other tribes were highly prized by the royal courts and noble houses of southern Europe. Recent archaeological research has revealed the remains of many Viking trading towns and villages throughout the Viking homelands dating from as early as 400. These market settlements were controlled, protected and ruled over by Viking tribal chiefs who came to be called Kings. The traders were protected so they gladly paid tolls to the king, who in turn, gave them protection from outside raiders by buying more warrior fighters to protect the settlement. Farmers were attracted to the area close to the trading posts as they too welcomed the protection of the tribal kings and the ready market for their surpluses in the trading towns or villages. These settlements as they prospered attracted skilled craftsmen in wood, ivory amber and metal as well as weavers of fine woollen goods to provide finished goods of high quality for trade. All these craftsmen were ready to pay dues to the king in return for the same protection he provided for all in the settlement. So there grew up thriving tribal trading, craft centres and farming communities close to the seas around Scandinavia. The inhabitants were happy under the rule of tribal chiefs and their protective warriors and the towns and Kings flourished due to their ship borne trade.

## The Viking Ships

Cave paintings from many coastal sites in southern Norway dating from about 1000 B.C. reveal boats made with sturdy wooden ribs covered with skins, used for fishing. The oldest wooden ship found so far in Scandinavia dates from 300 B.C. It has five wooden planks fastened together with stitching and a boat length keel board for easy beaching on the shore of any fjord. By 400 long wooden clinker boats with rowlocks for 30 oars each side and a heavy wooden keel piece, as well as a high bow and stern prow were the direct precursors of the classic Viking boat. What added the extra speed and manoeuvrability to these boats was the addition of huge rectangular sails and a shaped and weighted keel with a very shallow draught. Boats dug up at Gokstad and Oseburg in Scandinavia have these vital factors that lead to the Vikings success as raiders - they were faster than any other European ship having both sail and oar power - and their shallow draught meant that they could be sailed or rowed right up rivers to inland towns. They were ideal ocean going landing-craft for armies, being able to land warriors and horses anywhere inland almost with as much ease as the modern helicopter lands attacking forces. In retreat they could hide way up estuaries where no other ships or boats had a shallow enough draught in the water to follow. No wonder the sagas and poems of the Vikings contain so many splendid tales of the seafarers and their mighty ships.

## The Viking Raids on Britain

Suddenly in 793 the Vikings burst into fury, raiding coastal monasteries and settlements of north eastern England. Why was there such a sudden and violent a series of raids on Britain which were followed by years of raiding and settlement by the Viking peoples of Norway, Sweden and Denmark? Many reasons can be advanced. First the Viking ethos that Kings were bounteous providers for their subjects, especially their warriors, meant new treasures always had to be found so that Kings could be celebrated in saga and poem as the generous 'ring-givers'. Secondly Viking lore and cultural heritage dictated that warriors had to constantly prove themselves in battle and war-like deeds, so the attacks on England were ideal opportunities for them. Finally the amount of land available in the fjord areas of Scandinavia, coupled with a rich diet that produced strong and long-lived people meant that an increasing number of people were in competition for smaller and smaller pieces of land. When this was coupled with tribal rules that family lands had to be divided up equally amongst the male heirs it meant that there was an urgent need to find new settlement sites.

## Raids Become Invasions and Settlements

There was a lull between the attack on the north eastern coast of England in 793 and the next Viking onslaught. This came about because, either through accident or design, the Viking raiders concentrated their attacks between 800 and 830 on the northern

regions and isles of Scotland and the continent of Europe between present day Holland and northern France. Then, from 835, the Vikings, particularly those originating from Denmark, returned to concentrate their attacks on northern England. Perhaps their spies or raiders had told them that this was an easier area to plunder or a softer target. Whatever, the Vikings attacked the northern Saxon Kingdoms of Mercia and Northumbria from 834 onwards. They conquered the area and then their followers moved in to settle and dominate the region. By 870 they were free to move south with their attacks to conquer East Anglia. Again settlers followed the initial conquest setting up villages and trading centres and farming the land. These lands to the Vikings were easy and fertile after the harshness of their steep fjorded homelands in Scandinavia. Thus it was that from 850 the Vikings or Danes, as their contemporary Saxons called them, came to settle in many areas of England to the north and east of a line from modern day Chester to the Thames estuary. This area by agreement with both the Saxon inhabitants and the Viking invaders came to be recognised as Dane Law or the area of Danish and Viking influence.

## King Alfred resists the Viking Advance

Most Saxon rulers throughout Britain seemed to carry out a dual policy towards the Viking invaders. First, resist as far as was possible, then retreat to a defensible position, then barter land or wealth or palaces with the avenging hordes of Vikings to placate or satisfy them. By 876 the Danish Vikings had conquered all of northern England, established their main trading and administrative centre at Yorvik (modern day York) and were free to invade and fight the Saxon King of Wessex, Alfred, and his part time Saxon army. Under their Danish king Guthrum,. the Danish Vikings led attack after attack on the ports, towns and villages of Alfred's rich kingdom of Wessex. Alfred realised he could not beat the Danes in open battle, so he raided their raiding parties. After periods of skirmishing he and his men would retreat to the marshy area of the wetlands of present day Somerset.

Finally hemmed in here all looked lost for the Saxons. But then Alfred emerged from his marshland hideout refreshed with a fresh levy of troops and attacked the forces of Guthrum near Chippenham in Wessex. This time it was the Vikings who were forced back into the area of Danelaw north and east of the River

# Background Information for Class Lessons

Thames. Moreover these fierce pagan Vikings were forced to be baptised and to recognise the supremacy of the Christian faith.

## Saxon Kings reclaim most of England

Whilst Alfred's victory secured the south and west of Britain, a new threat came to the northern regions, when an alliance between the Viking kings of Dublin and Northumbria brought hordes of Irish Viking settlers to the north west of Britain. After Alfred's death in 899 his son Edward the Elder won a decisive battle against the Northumbrian Vikings at Tettenhal in the present day west Midlands in 910. After this victory the Saxon's employed a tactic of building fortified boroughs, slowly moving northwards their control of previously Viking held Danelaw. Edward's son, Athelstan, continued the successful campaigns against the Vikings eventually sacking Viking York in 927. By 934 the Viking kings of Ireland and King Constantine of Scotland joined forces, invaded the Northumbrian coast, recaptured York and swept into the Midlands of England where at the battle of Brunanburgh, a site now lost to history, King Athelstan with his Mercian and Wessex forces totally wiped out the Viking threat killing 5 kings and 7 earls in a day's fighting in 937 From this time on the Viking's control of the north ceased and the Viking kingdom's of Northumbria and York came to be ruled by a succession of Saxon earls protected by the strong forces of the Saxon Kings of Mercia and Wessex, Eadred and Edgar, who can be regarded as the first Kings of the whole of England. Many Viking settlements remained throughout the north but they were forced to pay allegiance to the Kings of England and live under Saxon jurisdiction.

## A Weak Saxon King invites renewed Viking Invasions

When Edgar died his 10 year old son Ethelred, known to history as Ethelred the Unready (really the Rede-less or No Counselled), came to the throne. The message of a weak King of England spread throughout the whole Viking world and within two years the first of many fresh Viking raids and invasions was under-way again. In 980 Southampton and the Isle of Thanet were ravaged and Cheshire overrun by Viking raiders from Denmark and Ireland respectively. Throughout the 980's Viking summer raids became the norm for Saxon coastal or riverside villages and towns. In 991 these niggling raids became an all out invasion. Olaf Tryggvason arrived in the Thames estuary that summer with an invasion army of ninety-three warships. He defeated the local Saxon forces at the Battle of Maldon, famous for the Saxon poem celebrating the bravery of a tribe and its leader in warfare, even in defeat. Ethelred immediately sought to placate the invaders by a negotiated settlement, the main terms of which were the payment of twenty two thousand pounds in gold and silver paid to the invading army to go away. This 'Danegeld' payment went directly to raising fresh invasion forces for the next onslaught. Four years later came a different Viking raiding party with a large invasion fleet, led by the Viking King of Denmark, Svein Forkbeard. London was its target, but beaten back by its stout resistance, the fleet of ninety four ships raided all along the south coast, frequently mounting their horses and raiding inland. Ethelred offered them terms of winter quarters in Southampton and food for the winter plus sixteen thousand pounds in coinage, all for a temporary cessation of hostilities. This pattern of professionally organised large invasion fleets attacking England and either returning with loot or cash for a temporary cessation of hostilities was repeated annually with an escalating scale of payments to pay off the invaders. By 1002 the price of the payoff had risen to £24,000, by 1007 it was £36,000. The year 1010 saw the Viking King of Norway Olaf the Fat pulling London bridge down immortalised in a nursery rhyme. 1011 was the nadir of Saxon hopes for in that year the Vikings captured Canterbury, and its Archbishop, sought and got a ransom for him of £48,000, then killed him in a drunken orgy. It is little wonder that vast quantities of Saxon coinage from these years has been found in grave hoards throughout Scandinavia.

## A Viking King of England becomes Ruler of the Empire of the North Sea

In July 1013 Svein Forkbeard, accompanied by his eighteen year old son Knut, set sail from Denmark at the head of an enormous Viking invasion fleet heading for England. The Fleet's first port of call was in Northumbria where the Vikings of the old Danelaw swore allegiance to Svein. Next the fleet sailed up the Thames but was repulsed by a strong Saxon response. So Svein moved target attacking the Wessex coastal settlements. His success here led to the Wessex earls surrendering to the Viking forces.

Inland forays soon led the Mercians to accede to the Viking Dane's superiority. Svein returned to prepare an assault on London. By way of response Ethelred fled with his family to Normandy. Svein was now King of England in all but name, but his triumph was short lived as he died in February 1014. Ethelred was recalled from Normandy promising just government and justice for all. The young Knut thought it prudent to return his invasion force to Denmark, where his older brother had been installed as King in succession to their father.

Knut was to return, though. In late 1015 he led a force of two hundred ships for yet another invasion of England by the Viking Danes. By April 1016 Knut was marching on London for a final showdown with Ethelred, only for the latter to die. London submitted, proclaiming Knut as their King. Edmund Ironside the next possible Saxon rival fought a series of inconclusive skirmishes with the Viking invaders, only to die in November 1016 before any strong Saxon resistance could rally around him to ward off the intruders. So on 30th November England had its first Viking King the young Knut.

Knut is best known for the legend of his rebuke of the waves from the edge of the tide seated on his throne. His courtiers had assured him he could rebuke the waves. Knut wished to show them up as merely fawning fools so he took part in the farce, and was covered by the incoming tide. Or perhaps the legend, recorded by Saxon chroniclers, shows some fine old Anglo-Saxon prejudice, never quite forgiving Knut for being a Viking, and secretly seeking to humiliate him through the story. A more Viking version is that Knut acknowledges that the power of the waves was from God, which all true Vikings knew from their heritage. Knut was to bring twenty years of much needed peace to England. He reissued English and Viking laws which emphasised impartial justice and the proper rights of individual people. Throughout his twenty year reign Knut courted the church, recognising it as the institution which could heal the wounds of centuries of strife. Threats from abroad were repulsed with ease, respect for Kingship was restored, firm government was the order of the day. Enemies died, and those who supported the new monarchy prospered.

It is a measure of Knut's greatness that he was immediately acceptable to all and built a more united peaceful Kingdom. In 1019 Knut hurried to his homeland, Denmark, to claim the throne when his elder brother died. In 1028 he invaded Norway forcefully to drive Olaf the Stout from the throne. It is characteristic of Knut that he only attacked Olaf and the Norwegian Vikings when they had just retreated battered and bruised from a thoroughly unsuccessful foray into the vastness of Russia. For a few short years this civilised Viking became ruler of a North Sea Empire that many Vikings had sought but only he achieved. When he died in 1035 the Minster at Winchester was rebuilt in fine strong Norman (continental Norse) style, full of Viking power and strength, as a place fit for this hardy yet shrewd Viking Emperor.

## The End of the Viking Era in Britain

By 1035 England was ruled by a Saxon again, Ethelred's son Edward the Confessor, home again from his exile with his maternal grandparents in Normandy. England experienced a calm of sorts, but undercurrents were emerging that would disturb the future succession after the death of the childless and saintly Edward. A Viking Dane Godwin had arrived in Wessex in the weak years of Ethelred. He soon established and expanded a power base in Wessex until his earldom included all of southern England. From this power base he and his argumentative Viking sons Harold and Tostig Godwinson began to seek to run the whole country. The weak Edward allowed them to act for him. Sibling rivalry saw Tostig build his own power base in the north amongst the settlers of Viking ancestry, greedily acquiring lands and allegiances throughout Mercia and Northumbria. Meanwhile, his elder brother consolidated his hereditary holding in Wessex and Anglia, as well as seeking to control the Government of the whole country from London, on behalf of the weak King Edward. With the approaching death of the childless Edward, four power greedy, strong men of Viking origins were to fight for the most prized of all Viking prizes - England - in 1066. From Norway came a successful marauder of Russia, Harald Hardrada. Bitter and seeking family revenge came Tostig supported by northern earls of Viking descent. He allied with Harald Hardrada and planned an invasion of England from the north east. With his Viking earls from the south, Harold Godwin claimed the throne of England. Then he raced north to defeat his brother and Harald Hardrada at Stamford Bridge. After a hurried journey south, Harald Godwin died in the battle of Hastings. His conqueror was William of Normandy, a Viking descendent, who arrived to claim England in that most Viking way - in a fleet of Viking ships.

## Weapons and Warfare

A three dimensional Viking wall, featuring brightly coloured shields in red and yellow, could provide the framework for a class display of Viking arms and armour. Let the children decorate Viking axes, spears and swords made from black card with Viking swirling patterns in gold, silver or bronze. Add to this, bronze or pewter coloured helmets decorated with black swirling patterns and you will have a dazzling display fit for the school's entrance. Children's research could be channelled into making a class display of a battle between the Saxons and Vikings, showing off individual children's coloured observational drawings in a dramatic panorama.

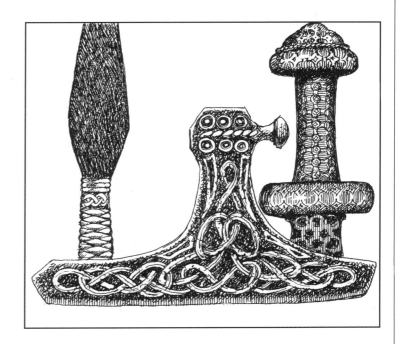

## Ships and the Sea

The Vikings were superb ship makers, who created many different types of ship for different purposes. Children's research should bring out the different designs of fishing, trading, and raiding boats. A class art project could have examples of all boats sailing in a choppy sea populated with fish and monsters of the Viking sagas portrayed in swirling interlocking Viking patterns. A different dramatic seascape class display could be created by portraying a Viking chieftain's burial at sea with his fiery warship sailing into a blazing sunset.

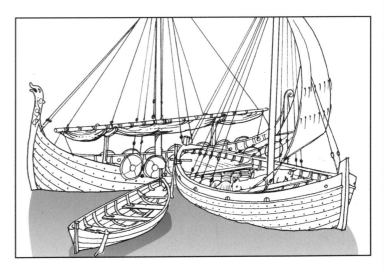

## Portraits

Head and shoulder shapes of Viking warriors, traders, settlers, farmers, craftsmen and Viking women will give the children opportunities to practise their portrait drawing skills. Discuss the differing moods and facial expressions of the raiders and the raided, traders and their customers, craftsmen and apprentices, men and women so that the children will improve their ability to portray the human face in its many aspects. These portraits could then be the inspiration for a class display of Viking characters with the children's character descriptions from a Literacy exercise mounted beside the relevant portrait.

## Buildings

Although few Viking buildings survive, children can be shown the Viking influence in many old peasant houses, which have timber cruck frames and are formed of timber framed 'bays'. These buildings are direct architectural copies of Viking constructions.

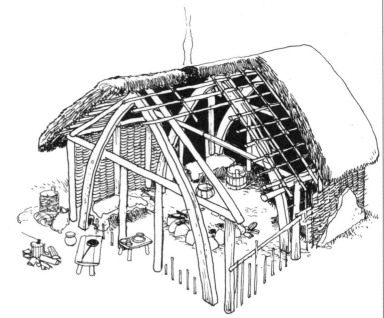

Viking homes made of cardboard boxes and other scrap material could have stones, wood, thatch or turf fixed onto their roofs and walls to copy the Vikings use of local materials in their buildings. Using individual children's models, a class 3D Viking village could be constructed. Children's drawings of Viking houses, backing such a display, would provide good practice in the use of perspective and three dimensional drawing.

## Decorative Animal Patterns

Viking craftsmen decorated stone, metal, and wood with animals whose bodies swirl, twist and intertwine in seemingly unending patterns. Examples of these beasts once photocopied could be used for children's observational drawing. Once coloured in the vivid basic colours used by the Vikings these animal patterns could provide borders and friezes around other Viking classroom displays. Using clay or plasticine the children could make three dimensional copies of small sections of this most popular of all Viking decorative craft.

## Coins

Because they were great traders and set up many different kingdoms throughout their world, the Vikings produced many outstanding coins. The wonderfully naive portraits of birds, animals, symbols and king's heads which mark the faces of these coins provide excellent art opportunities for children.

Observational drawings of these coins could be used to illustrate children's topic work. Using clay or plasticine, the children could create their own coins which when coloured gold silver, or bronze, would make a wonderful Viking treasure display. Create a class Viking treasure chest out of a cardboard box painted as wood, with locks, bars and hinges in Viking style and have the children's coins pouring from it to form the class's own Viking archaeological remains.

## Jewellery

Both men and women in Viking times wore richly decorated jewellery. Brooches were worn on shawls, tunics and cloaks. Necklaces of coiled silver or gold wire were popular with men, whilst the women wore necklaces of beads made from coloured glass. Both men and women wore gold or silver finger rings often made of wire shaped into intricate Viking symbols. The children could mount gold or silver sprayed small pasta shapes onto card shaped as broaches with coloured foil paper interspersed as jewels. A safety pin stuck on the back would complete their product. Necklaces could be made from string twisted together and then sprayed gold, or from silver beads of shiny foil paper strung onto fine thread. Plasticine strips twisted into finger ring shapes, then covered in papier mache, painted and varnished would complete a set of Viking jewellery ready to be worn by the children on a Viking day.

## Clothes

Large cardboard cut outs of the human body could provide the model on which groups of children could collage brightly coloured wool or linen, then add fur fabric, and leather or simulated leather to clothe their Viking figure. Men would wear trousers held at the waist by a draw string. On top of these, a long straight tunic was worn with a belt. In colder weather a cloak sometimes of animal skins would be fastened at the shoulder by a brooch. Viking women wore long linen dresses either plain or pleated. Over this would be worn a woollen tunic fastened at the shoulder by a brooch. Over the tunic would be a shawl or cloak. Both men and women would wear hats of wool or animal skins in cold weather. Children might like to improvise their own Viking clothes for a Viking day in school. A further art activity associated with Viking clothes would be for the children to make their own weaving frame from very stiff card. A shuttle made from similar card could then be wrapped with scrap wool and the children could weave their own Viking-style material.

## Three Dimensional Art Work

Pottery bowls, jugs, storage jars and plates have all been found in archaeological excavations on Viking sites. Coils of clay or plasticine built up on a clay slab base into the shape that children have researched for their Viking artefact will be made even more authentic when the children smooth the outsides with their fingers. Viking clay remnants reveal dark brown, black and occasionally dark yellow glazes which the children could replicate with paint covered with varnish when dry. Further 3D work in clay or plasticine could be for the children to make part of a Viking artefact as above and then bury these in a box filled with sand. Their classmates could then be given the task of uncovering these partial artefacts and reasoning their use and name.

## Art from Viking Sagas

The main entertainment after any Viking meal was Saga telling. Saga means spoken, so there were men who learnt by heart the legends and tales of the Vikings. Their story telling was made more fascinating by the beasts, sea creatures, demons, witches, kings, warriors and dragons which they included in their stories. Vikings believed that everyone had a 'fylgja' or animal spirit which went everywhere with them. Sometimes the spirit would be mischievous, other times protective. These spirits featured in many of the Viking Sagas or word stories. Allow the children to sketch out their own Viking dragon, witch, beast, warrior etc., using swirl and interlocking styles of portrayal common to the Viking period. This can then be made into an illustrated and written saga or retold in true Viking Saga style to a range of differing audiences using the illustrations as props for the saga.

## Viking Gods and Goddesses

A large number of illustrations of artefacts concerning the Vikings way of worship and religion exist as do stories of the Gods and Goddesses. Allow children to research the art and artefacts of the Viking religion, so that they can produce their own drawings and paintings of an individual Viking deity. A class collection of these with informative labelling would make an excellent wall display. Alternatively allow the children to make their own 3D clay, plasticine, or junk model representation of a single God based on their research of Viking artefacts. These could be in the form of pendants which Viking men and women wore to give them the protection or power reputed to be characteristic of that God or Goddess.

## Christian Viking Artefacts

Many Vikings who came to settle in Britain adopted or adapted themselves and their beliefs to Christianity. They then produced their own Viking artworks, celebrating their new found religion. These artefacts are to be found throughout Britain. Large standing crosses have wonderful Viking interpretations of biblical stories on them. These were used to teach the faith being large visual aids in a way similar to later medieval stained glass windows and fulfilled a teaching mission. Many of these crosses had, around their base or on their reverse side, representations of Viking gods and legends as if their makers were ensuring their life after death in both Christian and Viking form. These same dual religious portrayals are also found on the Viking hogback gravestones found in many British churchyards. From their research into Viking carvings on gravestones and crosses, encourage the children to fill a large cross or hog back shapes of grey paper with their copies of Viking Christian figures and Viking gods. Remind the children that these artefacts were often divided up into sections with typical Viking swirling or interlocking patterns. A collection of these would form a realistic Viking burial display.

# Viking Time-Line

## Task A

Cut out each Viking shield and paste it near to the correct place on the Viking Time-Line on the next two pages. Some of the Viking shields do not have dates. You will have to research the dates from reference books.

## Task B

Add further dates and facts to your time-line as you study the Viking era.

The Viking, Rurik, Captures Novograd in Russia. 862

All Viking lands are recorded in a Book of Settlement. 1100

Vikings raid the monastery at Lindisfarne, England.

886 King Alfred of Wessex, England, gives Guthrum the Viking, land in Eastern England.

The Viking, Eric the Red, discovers Greenland.

886 Viking raiders capture York, England.

The Viking King of Norway, Harald Hardrada, is killed in battle at Stamford Bridge, England.

King Charles the Simple of France, gives Rollo the Viking, Normandy in France.

1035 The Viking Knut is King of England, Denmark, Norway and Sweden.

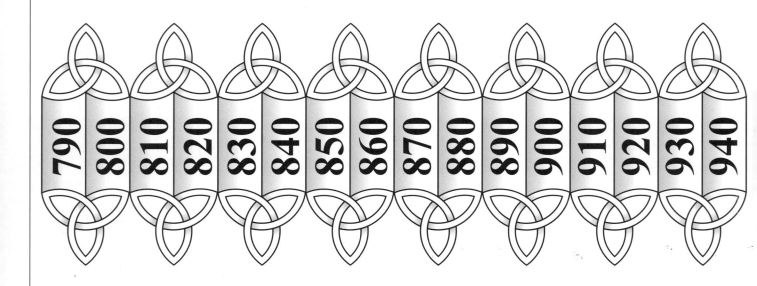

790 800 810 820 830 840 850 860 870 880 890 900 910 920 930 940

# Time-Line

950 | 960 | 970 | 980 | 990 | 1000 | 1010 | 1020 | 1030 | 1040 | 1050 | 1060 | 1070 | 1080 | 1090 | 1100

# Study different views about a Viking Raid on Lindisfarne, England. 793 A.D.

**A Viking Raider**

**An English Monk**

## Task A: Understanding that there are Different Views of the Same Event

Carefully read the statements below. Think about who might have made these comments, either a Viking Raider, or an English Monk. Cut out each statement and paste it under the correct character on your own sheet.

---

We could see the tower of their main building from our long boat when we were still out at sea.

---

We had heard that there were rich treasures on an island to the west of our home.

---

I was at prayer in the Church, when one of the farm workers ran in to say that there was a boat, with a large red striped sail, approaching the island.

---

There were many gold and silver plates and drinking cups in their main building. I was able to grab about five of these for myself. A man shouted at me, but I soon silenced him forever with a swift blow from my sharp axe.

---

I saw these fierce men kill many of my friends. I saw Brother John run away.

---

I could see our beloved church in flames as the raiders marched us down to their boats by the shore.

---

There were many men by the main building who had the tops of their heads shaved off. It was easy to grab the jewellery that hung around their necks.

---

I went out to greet the ship that was coming to our island shore. I was very frightened when the sailors from the boat rushed towards me waving axes and swords. They were shouting in a strange language.

---

The raiders from the ship chased all our men and women servants towards their ship. I think they wanted them as slaves. They were very rough with the women servants.

---

The people back home will be amazed at all the treasure we have captured.

---

## Task B: Describing Different Views of the Same Event

Imagine an attack on a Village in Britain by the Viking Raiders from Scandinavia. Write a Villager's view of the attack, then a Viking Raider's view of the same attack on the village.

# A Viking Raider's Kit

## Task: Information Writing

Research, in reference books, to help you find more information about the Viking Raider's Kit. The first one has been done for you. Against each piece of kit write three or more sentences; what the kit is made of, what it is used for and why you think it is important to the Viking Raider.

### The Helmet

*Note the leather and chain mail extension at the back to protect the neck.*

### Basic Clothing

A Viking Raider would wear loose fitting woollen trousers and a thick woollen shirt. Thick woollen socks and leather shoes would complete his normal clothing. On top of these he would wear either a padded leather tunic or a heavy chain mail tunic for protection. A decorated leather belt would have a sheath for his sword. In battle he would wear a metal helmet with a nose guard. At other times he would wear a felt hat.

### The Spear

-------------------------------
-------------------------------
-------------------------------
-------------------------------
-------------------------------
-------------------------------
-------------------------------

### The Sword

-------------------------------
-------------------------------
-------------------------------
-------------------------------

### The War Axe

-------------------------------
-------------------------------
-------------------------------
-------------------------------
-------------------------------
-------------------------------
-------------------------------

### The Shield

-------------------------------
-------------------------------
-------------------------------
-------------------------------
-------------------------------

# Were the Vikings Raiders, Settlers or Traders?

"I have heard that there are lots of rich places across the Great Sea. Erik the Wavebeater has been there, and he came back with lots of stolen silver. I want to build a ship and go raiding."

"I don't want to sail away from my fjord; there's plenty of fish to catch, and so many storms out in the big sea. A boat can easily sink.

"I barter furs from the hunters in the mountains until my boat is full, then I sail south, reach a distant city, and barter them for silver, gold and precious stones."

"I am the richest man in my village now. Crowds gather when we return from our raids on the churches of England. They are jealous of all the slaves I capture there."

"Last year I sailed down a great river to the east, to trade in a city where I saw a beast with a hump on its back."

"At our village meeting the village chief, Olaf, said that soon there will not be enough land for everyone. He wants some people to sail to Anglia to find land to live on. He says there is plenty of good land there."

"I have sailed into a great warm sea, and come back with oil that is so sweet to cook with, everyone will want to have some. I will make much with my bartering."

"My wife says we must buy a place on a boat for Anglia, so that we can find more land to farm. She wants all our sons to have a farm of their own, and there is no spare land for them here."

"Every time we raid villages in Wessex we see many rich farms with lots of land. I think that I will settle there soon. The Saxons fight back now each time we raid their homes."

"The Great Sea had huge waves and many people thought we would never see land. The women and children were screaming with fear. All were wishing we were back in the fjord."

## TASK A: Selecting information and recognising different views of the past

Cut out the pictures of the different Vikings and paste them onto separate pieces of A4 paper. Next, read the different statements, cut them out, and paste them under the picture of the Viking whose views, you think, they most closely match.

## TASK B: Using different sources to find out about the past

1  Research, in reference works, to find places that the Vikings raided in Britain.

2  Research, in reference works, to find places in Europe where the Viking Traders bartered goods.

# Information from Viking Artefacts

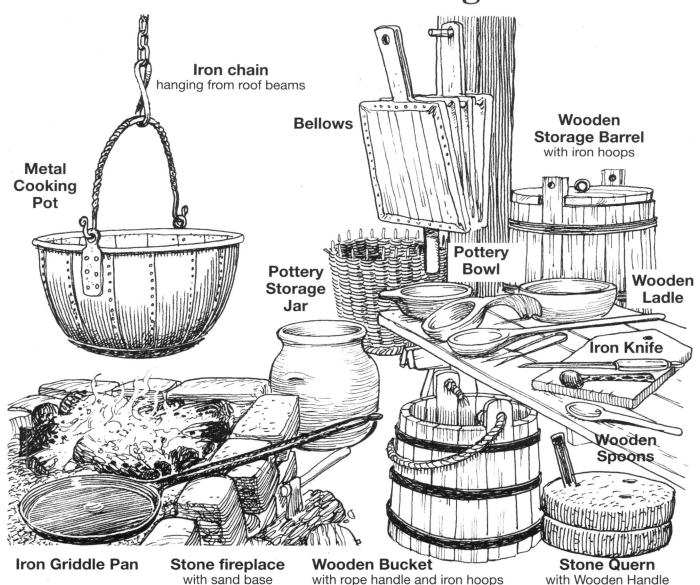

**Iron chain** hanging from roof beams

**Bellows**

**Wooden Storage Barrel** with iron hoops

**Metal Cooking Pot**

**Pottery Bowl**

**Wooden Ladle**

**Pottery Storage Jar**

**Iron Knife**

**Wooden Spoons**

**Iron Griddle Pan**

**Stone fireplace** with sand base

**Wooden Bucket** with rope handle and iron hoops

**Stone Quern** with Wooden Handle

## Task A

Study the Picture of Viking Artefacts then :

1   List the artefacts which were used to prepare food for cooking.
2   List the artefacts in which the Vikings cooked their food.
3   List the artefacts used by the Vikings for holding liquids.
4   List the artefacts in which food was stored.
5   What fuel do you think the Vikings used to provide heat for their cooking.

## Task B

1   List the utensils used in your home for preparing food, cooking food and the fuel used to heat your meals.
2   Do we still use any kitchen items that are similar to those used by the Vikings about a thousand years ago. Name some of them.

# Everyday Life of a British Viking Chieftain's Family

## The Longhouse

The chieftain and his family all live together in one big room of the longhouse. The room is always dark as the longhouse does not have any windows. It is smoky and smelly too as there is only a small hole in the ceiling to let out the smoke from the fire.

## Kitchen Storage

Close to the fire are wooden buckets to store water, milk, butter, cheese and grain. Pottery jugs and jars are used to store other items of food and drink. Joints of meat and whole fish hang from the roof beams above the fire smoke. This will preserve the meat.

## Lamps

Whale oil and animal fat are the fuel for the lamps held at the top of metal holders. Other lights are kept in soapstone lamps.

## The Fire

In the centre of the hall is a large rectangle of sand with a wall of small stones around it. On this a fire of wood or peat burns at all times. The women cook on the fire using metal pans.

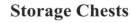

## Beds

The chieftain and his wife sleep in a wooden bed with straw mattresses and animal skins to keep them warm. Others sleep on platforms at the edge of the hall. They have the similar mattresses and coverings.

## Storage Chests

Spare clothing, jewellery and other precious goods are all kept in large wooden chests scattered around the hall.

## Eating Places

Wooden trestle tables with wooden benches can be moved around the hall and used for eating at or working on.

## Toilet Arrangements

Outside the hall is a frame of branches around a wooden bucket with a lid with a hole in it. This is the toilet which is emptied onto the land when it is full.

## Indoor Work

The women spin thread out of flax or wool. This they weave into cloth for clothes, wall hangings, or blankets, on a large wooden loom. The men may work with animal skins to make clothes and shoes by the light of the fire, or they may sharpen their tools or weapons. This work is done in times of bad weather, or in the dark winter days when the men and women are not involved in farm work.

### Task A: Reasoning Exercise

1. After careful study of pages 18 and 19 choose which home you would have preferred to have lived in during Viking times in Britain. Give several reasons for your choice. Write your answers in full sentences.

2. Study pages 18 and 19 again. Now list five things about the house that have changed from Viking Britain and five things that have stayed the same. Write your answers in full sentences.

# Daily Life in a Poor Viking Family's Town House

## The House

The house has a small and simple wooden frame. The gaps in the frame are filled with tree branches nailed across the frame. These are covered with mud which is then covered with lime. The roof is made of a thatch of reeds. The house has only one room.

## Storage

Wooden barrels and buckets, pottery jugs and jars and canvas sacks are used to store food and drink. They are kept close to the fire or on wooden shelves on the wall. Clothes, blankets and many food items are stored hanging from hooks in the roof.

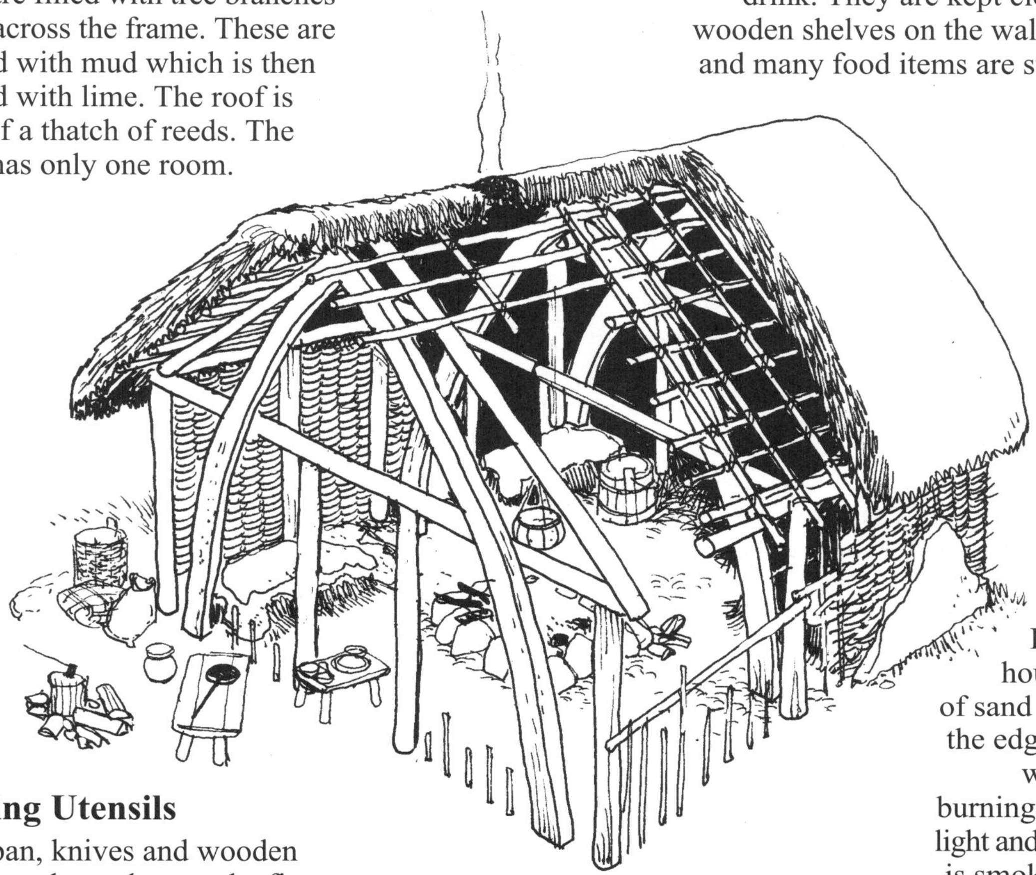

## Beds

Raised platforms of earth covered with straw or reeds make up the beds. Animal skins are used as bed coverings.

## The Fire

In the middle of the house is a raised bank of sand with stones around the edge. A fire fuelled by wood is always kept burning. It is used for heat, light and cooking. The house is smoky as there is only a small hole in the thatch to let the smoke out.

## Cooking Utensils

Metal pan, knives and wooden spoons are kept close to the fire for use. The people eat from wooden bowls.

## Furniture

Very simple wooden benches and boards are used as seats. They are the only items of furniture in the house.

## Washing

Most poor town houses are not far from a stream or river. The women wash the family's clothes on stones by the edge of the stream or river. The people rarely wash themselves. When they do, they wash in the river or stream.

### Task B: Find out about aspects of the period

Study the text and illustrations on pages 18 and 19 and then complete your own copy of the chart below in as much detail as you can.

| Topic | A Viking Chieftain's Hall | A Poor Viking's Town House |
| --- | --- | --- |
| Heating | | |
| Cooking | | |
| Lighting | | |
| Furniture | | |

# Artefacts tell us about the Vikings

## Task A: Reasoning Exercise

Study each artefact carefully, then complete each sentence after you have reasoned thoughtfully about its purpose, use and design. You may want to research in books to help you decide.

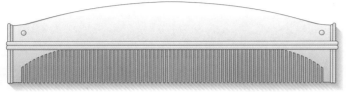

*Carved from a Deer's Antler*

### Artefact 1

I think that the Vikings would use this to _ _ _ _ their _ _ _ _. I think this because Viking craftsmen were highly skilled in carving, or turning combs, beads, buttons, needles, hair pins and ice skates from the antlers of deer. The material could be carved into very fine shapes and still remain quite strong.

One of the reasons why the Vikings came to Britain was to mine the precious gold and silver from its mountains and hills.

### Artefact 2

I think that this artefact would have been made of a precious metal like gold or _ _ _ _ _ _. The Vikings would have used these to fasten their _ _ _ _ _ _ together. I think this because

------------------------------
------------------------------
------------------------------
------------------------------
------------------------------
------------------------------
------------------------------
------------------------------

### Artefact 3

I think that Viking men would use this artefact to _ _ _ _ down trees. They might then use the artefact to _ _ _ _ _ the wood into a stool or a table or a piece of their Viking _ _ _ _ in which to sail away to distant lands.
I think this because

------------------------------
------------------------------
------------------------------
------------------------------
------------------------------
------------------------------
------------------------------

### Artefact 4

The Vikings were skilful farmers who grew many different cereal crops. They would use this artefact to _ _ _ _ _ _ _ their grain, which they would then make into their _ _ _ _ _.
I know about this artefact because

------------------------------
------------------------------
------------------------------
------------------------------
------------------------------
------------------------------

*Some words that may help you :-*
**chop, hair, shape, silver, cloaks, harvest, bread, comb, ship**

## Task B

Research in reference books to find four other Viking artefacts. Carefully draw them, and write about their design, giving your reasons for their use.

# Make your own Viking Cartoon Story

The Vikings gave many of their Kings and heroes nicknames, which tell us something about their character or about an incident in their life. Here are some of them drawn in cartoon style, with part of a script for a cartoon film about how they got their nicknames.

### Ragnar Hairy Breeches

A great hero, who hated the cold winters of the Viking lands, so he cut a wolf's skin up and made himself a pair of underpants. He wore them even in hot weather so no one liked to go close to him as he smelt sweaty.

### Sigtrid the One Eyed

Sigtrid was always peeping through holes in house walls to see what others were doing in private. Unknown to Sigtrid, a dragon had taken over the house in the village. Sigtrid peeped into the house...

### Harald Blue Tooth

One day Harald's wife was making a dye to colour her new dress blue. Harald, who was clumsy, came into the house, tripped over and fell, teeth first, into the blue dye. His teeth became blue, and always stayed that way.

### Ivor the Boneless

### Sigurd the Dragon Slayer

### Svein Forkbeard

## Task A:
### Imaginative writing about the past

Imagine you are the cartoon creator, complete the script for Sigtrid the One Eyed, and then provide scripts for the other Viking cartoons.

## Task B:
### Script writing

Make up a page of a Viking Comic providing your own drawings and script.

# Viking Women's Lives
## Cooking and Baking

### Grinding Grain

Viking women would grind oats, barley or wheat into flour for their bread using a stone quern with a wooden handle. This would be a daily job.

### Kneading Dough

The flour would be mixed in a wooden trough with water and some of the dough saved from the day before that had changed to a yeast to make the bread rise. Again this was an everyday job for Viking women.

### Baking & Cooking

There would be a large fire in the centre of all homes. The women would spend long hot hours over this to make their stews, broths and bread for the daily meals.

### Making Butter & Cheese

It was a woman's job to milk the family's sheep, goats and cows each day. Then she would have to stand and turn the milk in a wooden churn until it became butter. This was a long and hard job for Viking women. Cheese making would take even more of a Viking woman's time.

### Viking Women's jobs linked to Farming and Fishing

At busy harvesting, hay-making and seed sowing times of the year, Viking women would have to help out with these vital farm jobs. When animals were slaughtered for their meat it would be the women's task to salt the meat into barrels to preserve it or to hang it high over the fire to smoke it. Equally, it was the women's job to salt any fish caught, or to dry the fish on wooden racks in the sun to preserve them.

### Other important facts to remember about Viking Women's lives

- A Viking Chieftain's wife might have slaves to help her with the daily women's work.

- When the men were away on voyages, the Viking women would have to do all the farm work as well as their own work. Most Viking women lived on farms or in very small villages.

- Viking women were expected to teach the Viking children all the jobs of a Viking farm. There was no school.

- Viking women living in towns would have missed out on the farming tasks, but they would probably have had some craft job to do instead, linked to their family's trade or business.

### Task A: Interpreting Evidence from Different Sources

After careful study of the two pages about Viking Women, draw a large circle on a piece of A4 paper and divide the circle into twelve equal segments. Then draw and label in each segment the activities a Viking Woman might be working at throughout the hours she is awake. Add interest to the task by producing separate circles for the different farming and fishing seasons of the Viking year.

### Task B: Comparing and Contrasting Historical Evidence

Divide a separate sheet of A4 paper in half down its length. Put a title Viking Women at the head of one column and Modern Women at the head of the other column. First list neatly the tasks a Viking woman has to do daily, then in the other column, list the tasks a modern woman does in her day. When you have completed your task discuss the similarities and differences with your partner, group or classmates.

# Viking Women's Lives
## Making Clothes

Viking women wore their fair hair in long plaits, often held in place with a brooch or pin. They would cover their head for warmth with a scarf or cap made of linen material.

Viking women wore long dresses made of linen or wool. These were coloured using dyes made from plants and roots.

Over their dresses the Viking women wore a long linen tunic, like a long pinafore or apron. It was often held in place with a pair of brooches joined by a chain or a string of beads.

In cold weather or outside, Viking women would wear a woollen shawl or a cloak made of animal skins.

To keep warm, the Viking women would knit themselves long stockings. Their shoes would be made of leather or have knitted woollen tops and leather soles.

The number of rings, bead necklaces, brooches, armlets, bracelets and jewelled pendants that a Viking woman wore or possessed, would tell you how rich she and her family were.

**Viking Women's work connected to their own and their family's clothes.**

### Beating Flax

After the flax plant had been cut, the women soaked it for several days in water. Then they would beat it on a board so that it produced fine threads.

### Carding Wool

Once the wool had been shorn from the sheep, the Viking women would use long metal pronged combs to get any knots or burrs out of the wool. This made the wool easier to spin.

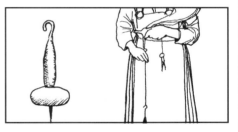

### Spinning Yarn

Viking women tied some wool to a stick and a spindle. They then spun the spindle and let it drop. This pulled out the wool, making it into thread. The thread is then gathered on the spindle.

### Collecting Dyes

Plants, flowers, roots, bark and some rocks are gathered and then ground into a powder by the Viking women to make dyes.

### Dying Yarns

The Viking women would fill a large wooden bucket with water, mix in their dye, then soak their spun yarn in the dye. They would wring it dry, ready for weaving and knitting.

### Weaving

Many Viking women had their own weaving loom. They would weave cloth in any spare moment. Their material could be made into sails, blankets or clothes.

# Viking words give us

**Viking words that describe the landscape (most of them are suffixes)**

**Ayre**
a gravel bank.

**–gata, gate**
a narrow passage or street or road.

**-beck**
a stream

**-gill**
a deep valley or ravine.

**-berg**
a hill (often changed in time to be spelt burgh).

**-holme or –hulme**
meadow by the water.

**Bla-, Ble- , Blo-**
black

**- katr**
a sandy bank (changed in time to be spelt as Cart)

**- brekka**
a hill (now spelt breck or brick).

**- byr, -by**
a cultivated dwelling.

**– myer -mere**
a marshy wood by a lake.

**-car**
marshy land.

**-ness**
a headland, land jutting out into the sea.

**-dalr**
opening or flat land between two hills, (now spelt –dale).

**–saetr**
a field on the mountainside (changed to be spelt –side).

**-ergh or –argh**
a hilly pasture, clearing in the woods.

**–sall**
a small mound.

**-thwaite**
a clearing in the woods.

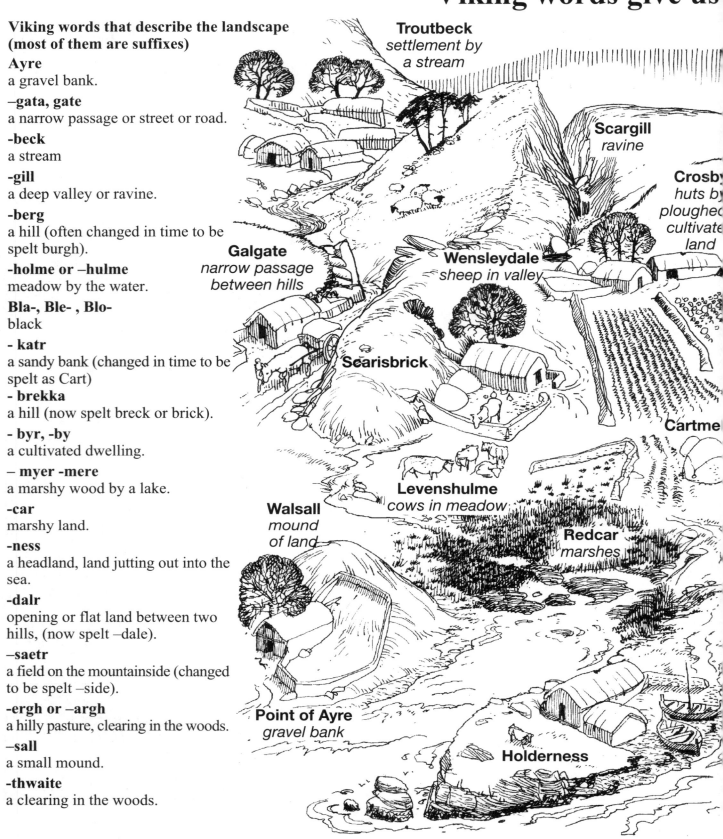

**Troutbeck**
*settlement by a stream*

**Scargill**
*ravine*

**Crosby**
*huts by ploughed cultivated land*

**Galgate**
*narrow passage between hills*

**Wensleydale**
*sheep in valley*

**Scarisbrick**

**Cartmel**

**Levenshulme**
*cows in meadow*

**Walsall**
*mound of land*

**Redcar**
*marshes*

**Point of Ayre**
*gravel bank*

**Holderness**

When a Viking raiding band found some area of land which they liked, they might choose to settle down there. They would build homes and give their new settlement a name.

Many of their names contained the name of the raiding party's leader as its first part, followed by a Viking word describing the sort of countryside that their settlement was in.

# ome of our place names

**Goosnargh**
*clearing in wood*

**Waberthwaite**
*clearing in wood*

**Ambleside**
*field on mountainside*

**Windermere**
*lake*

**Blackpool**
*dirtywater*

## Task A

Guess the leaders' names. Find them in the Viking place names on pages 24 and 25.

## Task B

Research in reference books, atlases, maps of Britain and local maps to find places in Britain that are of Viking origin (as above). Make your own list of these places, with the Viking meaning of part of the word written out to explain the place's Viking origin.

# Food in Viking Britain

## Evidence from Archaeological excavations - Yorvik Middens

Archaeologists excavating the Viking city of Yorvik, which lies about 10 feet beneath the modern city of York, found the remains of houses, workshops, warehouses and shops. Outside most houses they found piles of rubbish.

These piles were the remains of the middens of Viking Yorvik. These piles were really the dustbins or waste piles containing the scraps from many Viking meals.

## The Archaeological Finds from the Yorvik Middens

The archaeologists found the shells of hazel nuts, the shells of hens eggs, the pips of apples, the stones from wild cherries, plums and wild sloes. All these remains suggest a varied fruit and nut diet for the Vikings of Yorvik. The husks from the seeds of rye, barley and oats tell us that the bread Yorvik's Vikings ate was made of these cereals.

Large quantities of the shells of mussels and cockles were found. There were enough to suggest these were part of the staple diet of Viking Yorvik.

Many Fish bones were dug up. Archaeologists can tell us that these came from trout, salmon and other fish which would have been found in the River Ouse in York.

In the Middens were found the bones of many animals. Scientists have identified the bones of cattle, sheep, pigs, rabbits, pigeons, ducks and deer. This suggests that the people of Yorvik ate a very wide variety of meat.

## Other Yorvik Archaeological finds which tell us about Viking eating habits

The many barrels found in some places in Yorvik suggest that there were homes which specialised in the production of beer.

Outside the backs of some homes in Yorvik the archaeologists found wicker basket shapes in the form of beehives. These suggest that the people of Viking Yorvik sweetened their food and drink with honey from beehives.

Small three legged stools at just the correct height for milking cows and goats as well as the remains of many wooden buckets suggest that milk was part the every day diet of Viking Yorvik.

Stone querns or grinding stones with wooden handles show the archaeologists that most households made their own bread from various grains.

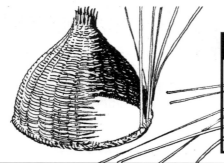

### Task: Reasoning Exercise

1  Using the information above, make up a day's menu card for a Viking Family.
2  Conduct a survey of your class or friends to find their 'TopTen' favourite Viking dishes.

# A Busy Trading Day at Viking Yorvik

**Instructions.**     Make your own pop up Viking Trading City and see the cargoes come and go.

1  Copy pages 27, 28 and 29 onto thin card.

2  Use masking tape to join pages 28 and 29 together as shown in the diagram.

3  Research in reference books to find pictures of Viking traders, merchants, sailors, ships, houses and craft workshops, then carefully colour the Viking background on pages 28

4.  Cut out around the ship shape on page 27. Paste flap (a) to (a) on page 29. Fold the ship up along the dotted line. Fix strip (b) behind the ship, and on to page 28 to make it stand up.

5.  Write your own report about the imports and exports and the arrivals and departures at your busy Viking Yorvik city in the space provided on page 29.

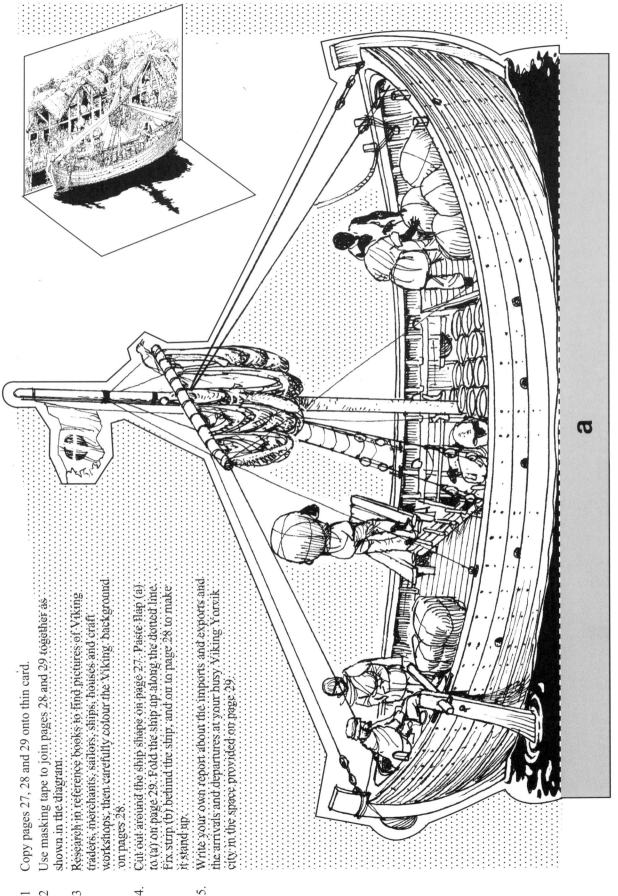

Fix to back ground     Fix to back of boat

a

# Yorvik Traders Exchange Treasures from all around the Viking World

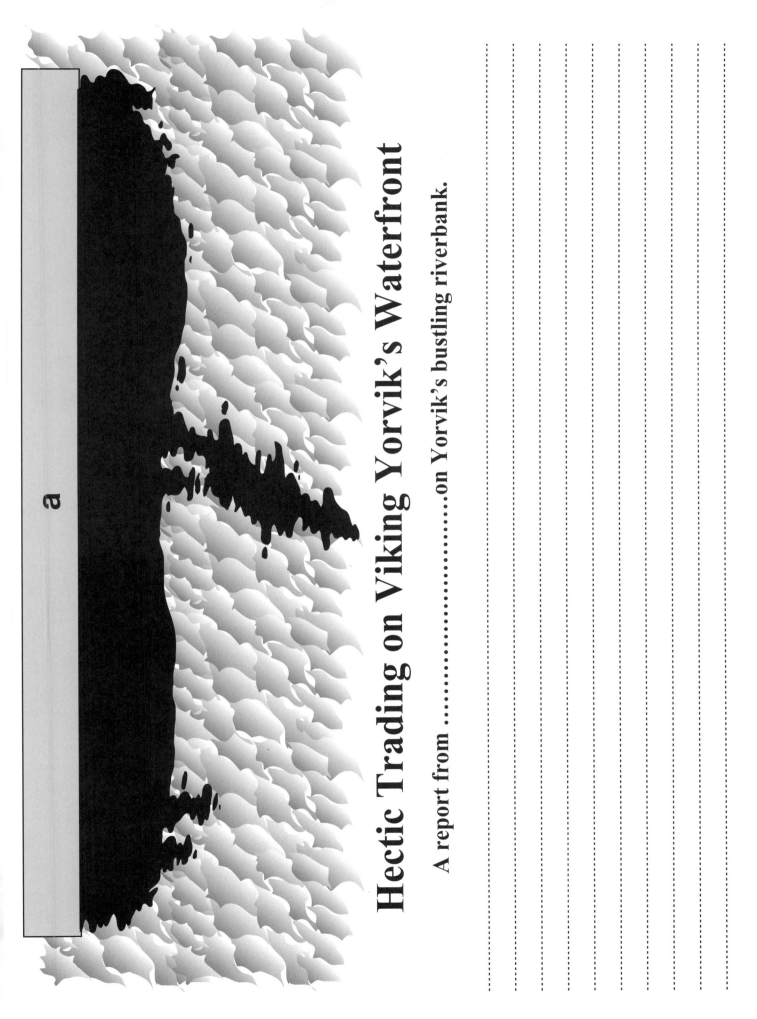

# Hectic Trading on Viking Yorvik's Waterfront

**A report from** ........................**on Yorvik's bustling riverbank.**

# Write your very own Viking Saga

Imagine yourself in a Viking chieftain's hall, with a bright fire lighting up the listeners' faces clustered around the hearth stones. The Chieftain bemoans the absence of the clan's Saga teller. He calls for you to take over the role of story teller and regale the clan with a new and exciting Viking saga. Your audience, the Viking family clan, will expect a story involving a voyage in a Viking ship, with its brave crew, through storm and tempest. Dragons, demons, weird beasts, terrifying warriors, threatening sharp beaked birds and wart encrusted trolls from the deep recesses of the earth should appear in your story. But your heroes must triumph over the forces of evil and rescue the clan chief's beautiful daughter from the evil monster's lair in some dark cave.
Start your Saga here:

-------------------------------------------------------------------
-------------------------------------------------------------------
-------------------------------------------------------------------
-------------------------------------------------------------------
-------------------------------------------------------------------
-------------------------------------------------------------------
-------------------------------------------------------------------
-------------------------------------------------------------------
-------------------------------------------------------------------
-------------------------------------------------------------------
-------------------------------------------------------------------
-------------------------------------------------------------------
-------------------------------------------------------------------
-------------------------------------------------------------------
-------------------------------------------------------------------
-------------------------------------------------------------------
-------------------------------------------------------------------

You may want to continue your Saga overleaf, or on a separate sheet of paper.

# THE VIKING RAIDERS, TRADERS & SETTLERS GAME

## For up to 4 players

**The Vikings were very skilled sailors, who travelled far and wide to find rich goods to bring back to their Viking homelands in what is now modern Norway, Sweden and Denmark**.

● Sometimes they went as **Raiders** (they were really like robbers or pirates).

● Sometimes they went as **Traders**, to exchange their goods for other goods they did not have in the Viking homelands.

● Sometimes they went as **Settlers** to find more or better lands where they could set up new farms, villages and towns.

## Aim of the Game

You are in turn a **Viking Raider**, a **Viking Trader**, and a **Viking Settler**.

**First,** you have to visit different countries where the Vikings raided, bringing home to the Viking homelands four pieces of treasure. **Next,** you have to trade in different places, exchanging your treasure for four different products to bring home. **Finally,** you are to sail out and discover a place for your family to settle where there is lots of land to set up a new Viking village. You must keep a **'Ships Saga'**(or log) of the places you have visited and the dangers you have met.

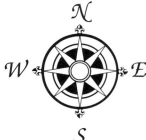

NB

It is recommended that the map is photocopied larger (say A4 to A3) or larger still, then mounted on stiff card.

## How to play the Game

1  Your teacher sets the time limit for your game.

2  Each player throws the dice once. Start from the Viking Homelands. The person with the highest score chooses his/her ship, shakes the dice, and moves that number of places in the direction of places where the Vikings raided, marked by ⚔. Collect one counter/treasure from each battle site.

3  Each player follows in turn, collecting 1 counter from the raider's site visited, When you have 4 counters, return to the Viking Homelands.

4  After that, each player sets out as a Viking trader shaking and travelling that number of places where the Vikings traded, marked by ●. When you arrive there, you pick up cargoes which you have bartered for with your raider's treasure, exchanging 1 treasure counter for one cargo of goods. Your ship can only carry 4 cargoes again. Then you return to the Viking homelands.

5  After that you set out as a Viking Settler shaking your dice and moving that number of places, this time you are looking for a place to set up a new Viking village marked by ●.

6  The winner is the first player to settle in a Viking settlement. In the event of a tie your teacher will decide the winner based on the best 'Ships Saga'.

## You will need

● A dice

● A shaker.  Red, blue, green, and white counters, placed in the counter space on the map board

● The Map on pages 32 and 33 pasted on to stiff card.

● A piece of paper with 'Ship's Saga' written on it for each player, and a pen and pencil.

● Ship Shapes for each player.

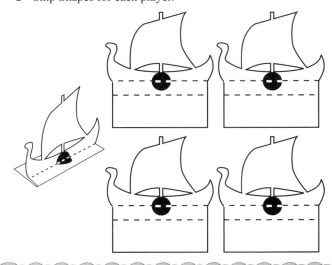

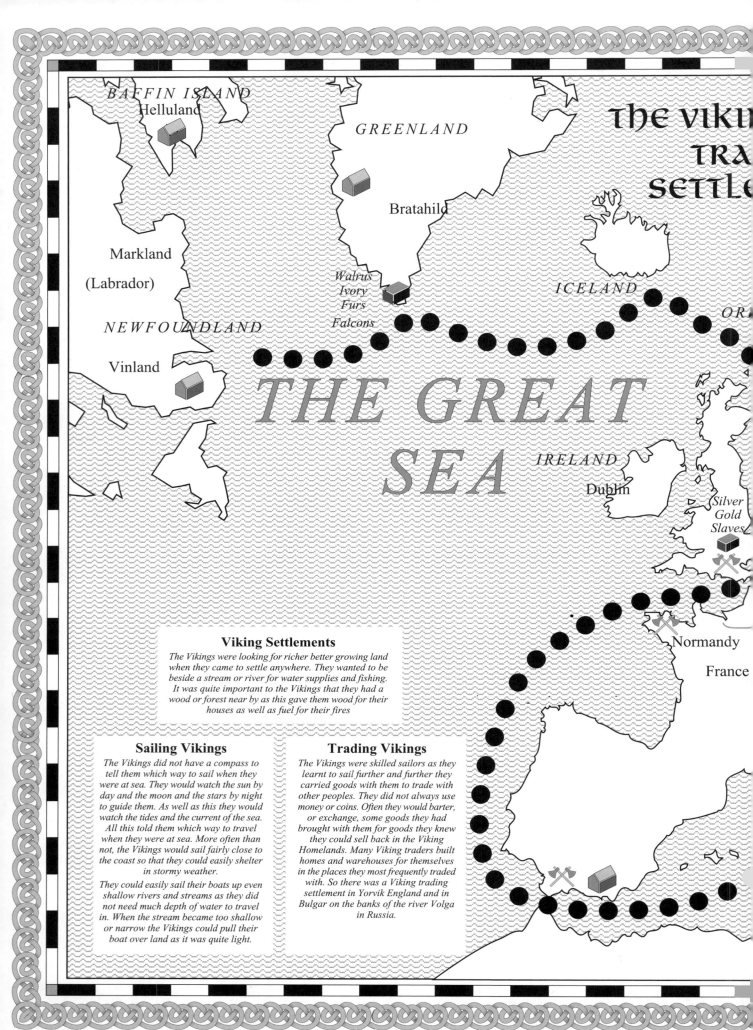

BAFFIN ISLAND
Helluland

GREENLAND

Bratahild

Markland

(Labrador)

Walrus
Ivory
Furs
Falcons

ICELAND

OR

NEWFOUNDLAND

Vinland

THE VIKI
TRA
SETTLE

THE GREAT

SEA

IRELAND

Dublin

Silver
Gold
Slaves

Normandy

France

## Viking Settlements

*The Vikings were looking for richer better growing land when they came to settle anywhere. They wanted to be beside a stream or river for water supplies and fishing. It was quite important to the Vikings that they had a wood or forest near by as this gave them wood for their houses as well as fuel for their fires*

## Sailing Vikings

*The Vikings did not have a compass to tell them which way to sail when they were at sea. They would watch the sun by day and the moon and the stars by night to guide them. As well as this they would watch the tides and the current of the sea. All this told them which way to travel when they were at sea. More often than not, the Vikings would sail fairly close to the coast so that they could easily shelter in stormy weather.*

*They could easily sail their boats up even shallow rivers and streams as they did not need much depth of water to travel in. When the stream became too shallow or narrow the Vikings could pull their boat over land as it was quite light.*

## Trading Vikings

*The Vikings were skilled sailors as they learnt to sail further and further they carried goods with them to trade with other peoples. They did not always use money or coins. Often they would barter, or exchange, some goods they had brought with them for goods they knew they could sell back in the Viking Homelands. Many Viking traders built homes and warehouses for themselves in the places they most frequently traded with. So there was a Viking trading settlement in Yorvik England and in Bulgar on the banks of the river Volga in Russia.*

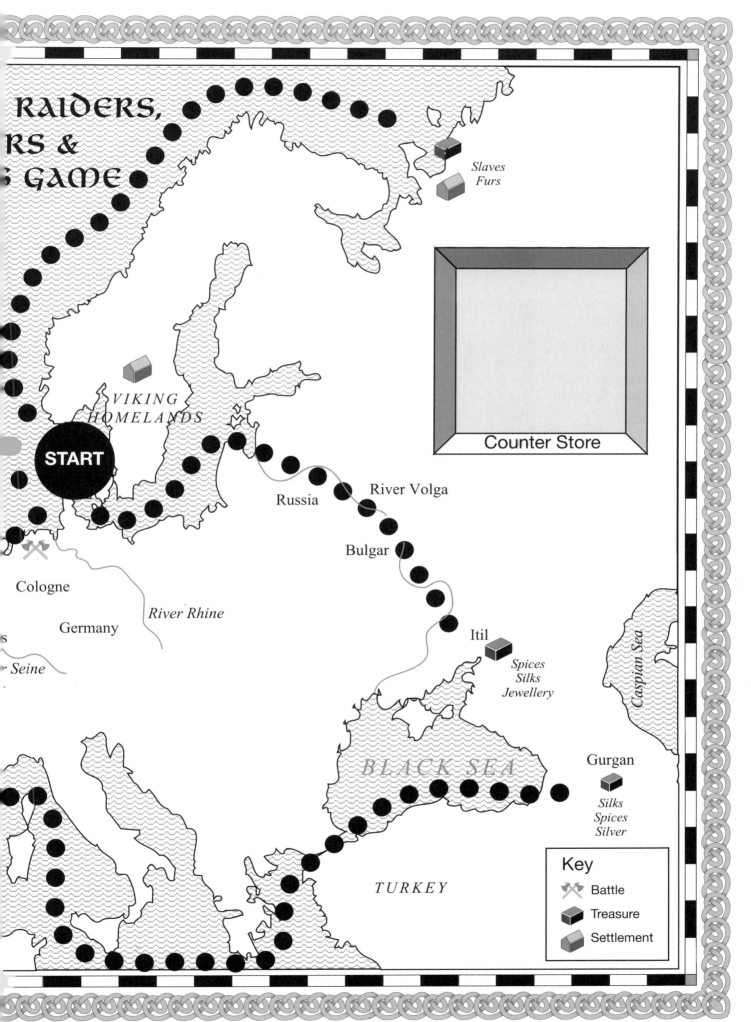

RAIDERS,
RS &
GAME

Slaves
Furs

Counter Store

VIKING
HOMELANDS

START

River Volga

Russia

Bulgar

Cologne

Germany

River Rhine

Seine

Itil

Spices
Silks
Jewellery

Caspian Sea

BLACK SEA

Gurgan

Silks
Spices
Silver

TURKEY

Key

⚔ Battle

Treasure

Settlement

# Viking Gods and Goddesses
## Evidence from Wood, Metal and Stone Remains

The chief God of the Vikings was Odin, who they believed had taken part in the creation of the world. He had only one eye having given up the other in exchange for the gift of the wisdom of the God. He was the master of magic who could see into the future and the past. He lived in his hall called Vallhalla, which means 'hall of the dead'. All Viking warriors wished to go to Odin's hall when they were killed in battle. Odin had two ravens, Huginn (Thought) and Muninn (Memory). Odin sent them out each day to fly all over the world and report back to him about what was happening in the world.

The Valkeries were Odin's female helper goddesses, whose job it was to visit every battle site and choose which warriors were to die in the battle. The Valkeries would then take the dead to Odin's hall where they would serve the warriors with horns filled with drink.

Thor was the Viking god of thunder and lightning. He had his own day in the week - Thursday. His weapon was a mighty hammer Mjollnir (or lightening). With this weapon he would slay giants and other evil creatures. He was the protector of all Gods and human beings. He killed the evil sea serpent Midgard so making the seas safe for the Vikings to sail over.

Frey and Freya were the brother and sister God and Goddess. Frey was the god of nature. The Vikings made sacrifices to him to make sure that the sun shone, the crops grew and all was peaceful. Freya was the goddess of love and of dead women. When women died they didn't go to Odin's Vallhalla but they joined Freya in her fortress hall to dance and feast forever.

*A wooden carving of Odin from a church at Heggan Norway.*

*A Valkerie from a gold drinking horn once owned by the Danish royal family.*

*Thor holding his hammer, Mjollnir. A stone carving in Reykjavik, Iceland.*

*Frey and Freya from a stone carving found on Orkney.*

## Task: Interpreting Evidence from different sources

**Carefully read the statements below and from the evidence above decide whether each statement is True, False or there is No Evidence for you to decide. Write a reason for your choice to go with each statement.**

1   The Vikings made their statues of the gods and goddesses from wood.

2   Odin was the Viking God of War.

3   The Vikings thought Thor came in the lightning and thunder.

4   Archaeologists know a lot about Viking gods and goddesses because Freya told them.

5   Thor killed the sea serpent Midgard with his hammer Mjollnir.

6   Viking women liked the goddess Freya best of all the Viking gods.

7   We know what the Vikings thought their gods looked like from carvings on wood, stone and metal.

8   Odin had two Ravens who reported happenings in the Viking world to him.

9   The Valkeries were thought to have visited the battlefields of Viking times.

10  We know about the legends of the Viking Gods and goddesses from Viking Sagas.

# Make a Viking Newspaper

On this page you have two news reports plus pictures from your illustrators.

Complete the next two pages ready for your newspaper's printing. Cut out and paste under your sub-editor's suggested titles. Notice that there are some story lines and pictures missing. As print day is tomorrow you will have to research, draw and write these items yourself to fill the empty column space.

All the subtitles you need are provided for you.

## Saxon Fighter speaks from a secret location in Wessex

Here deep in the lost marshes around the Island of Athelney, I have caught up with the remnants of King Alfred of Wessex's army. I spoke with Egbert, a Thane (or Lord) in Alfred's tiny army. When I asked him about the situation he replied, "We are in a real mess, the fierce Vikings have chased us all over Wessex. They have destroyed our villages. Alfred can't hold the army together. Many men deserted the army when they heard rumours about Vikings raiding their own area. They ran off home to defend their homes and families. Our brave King Alfred tried hard to keep our spirits up. He swore that we will win one day."

*Our Artist's drawing of King Alfred of Wessex hiding from the Vikings in an ordinary Saxon home. The woman is scolding Alfred for not watching her cakes cooking and letting them burn.*

*Our Artists impression of the Viking warriors from Denmark ready to raid a Saxon village.*

## From our reporter with Guthrum, fighting an elusive Alfred the Saxon

Guthrum, the battling leader of a large band of Viking warriors from Denmark, is tonight camped deep in the Kingdom of Alfred of Wessex. He spoke to our roving reporter, who is following the Viking attack on the last bastion of Saxon rule in southern England. "My men are in fine fighting condition, they have chased Alfred's forces across the whole of his kingdom. We have had many skirmishes with the Saxon forces, but they never stand and fight...... I think they are afraid of our Viking battle axes...... they keep running away from a proper fight with us."

# VIKING TIMES

Available monthly - June 878

Price 3 pennies

## Saxon King Alfred can't even bake a cake!

## Viking Warrior tells us why he plans to settle in Britain

The Beautiful Jewel of a Saxon King, a treasure any Viking would love.

Saxon Fighter speaks from a secret location in Wessex

# VIKING TIMES

Available monthly - June 878

Price 3 pennies

**Alfred makes peace with the Viking leader, Guthrum, after a battle near Chippenham, Wessex.**

------------------------------------------------

------------------------------------------------

------------------------------------------------

------------------------------------------------

------------------------------------------------

------------------------------------------------

------------------------------------------------

From our reporter with Guthrum
fighting an elusive Alfred the Saxon.

**Alfred orders that a book be made to tell the story of the Saxons in England.**

------------------------------------------------

------------------------------------------------

------------------------------------------------

------------------------------------------------

------------------------------------------------

------------------------------------------------

------------------------------------------------

------------------------------------------------

**Viking Raid on Saxon Village - our reporter describes the destruction**

------------------------------------------------

------------------------------------------------

------------------------------------------------

------------------------------------------------

------------------------------------------------

------------------------------------------------

------------------------------------------------

# Leif Eriksson the Great Viking Voyager

**Task: A Character Study of the Viking Who Discovered America**

Research, in reference books, to find out as much information as you can about Leif Eriksson. Then continue the character sketch of Leif Eriksson which has been started for you here.

Leif Eriksson was a Viking who lived in Greenland. There was not a lot of good land for growing food there, so Leif wanted to find a better place to live. One day a man called Bjarni Herjolfsson told Leif about a land to the west of Greenland that he had found when he was blown off course by a gale at sea. In 997 Leif decided to find this new land.

# King Knut - a Great Viking Hero

The facts about King Knut below have been mixed up. Cut them up and paste them in the correct order on a fresh piece of paper.

*Coin of King Knut*

Knut was the most successful Viking king of all. He became King of Sweden, Denmark, Norway and England. He was often known in England as Canute.

**Nov. 1016**
Edmund Ironside King of England dies and Knut becomes King of England.

**July 1013**
Knut and his father Svein Fork-beard invade Britain.

**1028**
Knut and his army drive King Olaf the Stout out of Norway. Knut becomes King of Norway.

**April 1016**
Ethelred the Unready, King of England, dies in London as Knut and his Vikings prepare to attack London

**1035**
Knut dies and is buried in Winchester Cathedral.

**995**
Knut born, his father is Svein Fork-beard, the Viking King of Denmark.

**1017**
Knut marries Emma, widow of Ethelred the Unready, so that the Saxons will support him.

**November 1016**
Edmund Ironside King of England dies in London and Knut is made King of England.

**1015**
Knut leads 200 Viking ships on a raid upon England.

**Task B: Fact or Fiction, Myth or Reality, True or False?**

Research in reference books to find as much as you can about the legend of King Canute ( Knut ) and the waves .

**February 1014**
Svein Fork-beard, Knut's father, dies. Knut becomes the leader of the Danish Viking raiders.

# Viking Writing and Language

## Viking Runes

The Vikings carved their writing on wood, stone, metal or bone with a sharp knife. They called their letters runes. Their alphabet was called the Futhark.

**Here are the Viking Runes:**

| a | b | c | d | e | f | g | h | ij | k | l | m | n | o | p | q | r | s | t | uvw | x | y | z |
|---|---|---|---|---|---|---|---|----|---|---|---|---|---|---|---|---|---|---|-----|---|---|---|
|   |   |   |   |   |   |   |   |    |   |   |   |   |   |   |   |   |   |   |     |   |   |   |

### Task 2

Now write your name in runes followed by 'cut this' in Runes on the bone carving below.

### Task 3

Now write your name in runes followed by 'made this magic snake' in Runes all around the serpent's body.

# Instructions for Model Building

## General instructions:

1   Ideally, the pages should be copied onto 160gsm card. This need not be white. Grey would be a good colour. If the copier will allow, the pages would benefit from being blow-up by 40% (from A4 to A3). This makes the models bigger, more atractive and easier to make.

  In the case of the house, page 45 should be copied **4 times** more than page 44 as you need 4 of everything on that page to make one house. The house is an ideal project for a small group of children.

2   If you intend to colour the models, it is advisable to do the colouring before the pieces are cut out from the sheet. The ideal medium is coloured pencils. Wax crayons can make gluing difficult and paint will warp the paper and hide the lines.

3   Cut along the solid outside lines. Score and fold along the dotted lines.

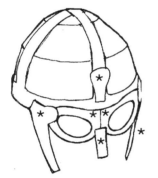

★ extra items

## Helmet (page 46)

1   Cut out the rim and straps a, b, c and front strap. Glue the straps onto the rim as show

2   Cut out the lower ring. Fold the tabs gently. Glue into a ring by fixing one end over the shaded area at the other end.

3   Now make the upper ring as (2) above.

4   Cut out the top. Make the cut from the edge to the middle as indicated and make a cone by gluing the plain side of the slit over the shaded area.

5   When all the parts are dry and firm assemble as indicated in the drawing. Align the joins. Fix the rim and straps last, and place, so that one of the straps covers the joins in the upper and lower ring. The short end of the front strap should hang down to protect the nose.

  The helmet is now finished if you are making a normal fighting helmet. If however you wish to make it into a ceremonial helmet, add the other pieces and any other decoration you might wish.

6   To make the extra elements, cut out all the 6 pieces and assemble. First join the spectacles together, then add the ear guards, and finally the decorative front pieces.

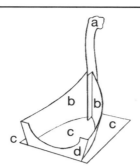

## The Boat Figurehead (page 47)

1   When you have coloured and cut out the pieces, one side of the stem will be blank. We have provided a reverse side but you can draw your own fiece head and decoration on that side if you wish. Carry out research, to see what you should draw

2   Fix the two pieces of the hull (b) with the planks on the outside, to the stem (a) where indicated on the printed side, and the same place on the other side.

3   When dry, fix the hull to sea (c) on each side. To do this use only alternate tabs to the underside of the sea, (these have been marked with a dot to help you). This will form the shape of the bow section.

4   Now fix the bulkhead (d) and deck to the tabs at the back. Fix the deck (planks uppermost) to the remaining alternate tabs.

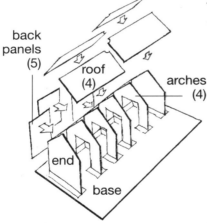

back panels (5)

roof (4)

arches (4)

end

base

## The House (page 44 and 45)

1   First, cut out the base on page 44.This forms the foundation for the house and indicates the correct position for each part of the structure.

2   Cut out the two ends of the house. They fold to give both an inside and an outside and the start of the outside back wall. Fix in position on the base board.

3   Next cut out 4 arches. These again are folded to make them double sided. Fix these in position on the base board between the ends of the house. You will see that they each provide another part of the inside of the back wall. They will be joined together next.

4   You will only require 5 back panels, (you will have 8). Fix these on the outside of the back, joining the inside arches together as you do so. The house now awaits its roof.

5   Cut out and fold double 4 roof sections. The thatch is on the top (outside). Each will provide a quarter of the roof. You may like to cut a hole in the centre of the finished roof to allow the smoke out (the chimney).

6   Finally, you can add the toilet. Place the fire and pieces of furniture in position. The model will benefit from some figures, which could be made from modelling clay.

NB The front of the house has been omitted to allow you to see inside.

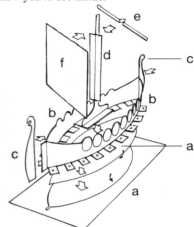

## The Long Boat (page 42 and 43)

  Before cutting out the pieces you may wish to add the decoration to the shields and the bow post. Even the sail may have featured some painted design. We have provided an empty circle in which you can place your design.

1   Cut out base (a). Next, carefully cut out the planked section in the middle. (This will be fitted inside the hull later)

2   Carefully cut out and assemble the hull (b) section.

3   Cut out and fold the stern and bow sections (c). Fix one on each end of the hull.

4   When the bow and stern are dry cut off the areas marked in black.

5   Fit planked area inside the hull, and the 'sea' outside, using alternate flaps on the hull sides.

6   Cut out, fold and glue the two mast parts together(d). The flaps on the mast are used to hold the sail in place.

7   Cut out the sail (f) and spar (e). Fold the spar, as shown in the diagram and fix, around the mast and to the back of the sail

8   If you wish to add oars, punch holes in the hull down either side between the shields and place sections of craft straw through the holes to imitate the oars.

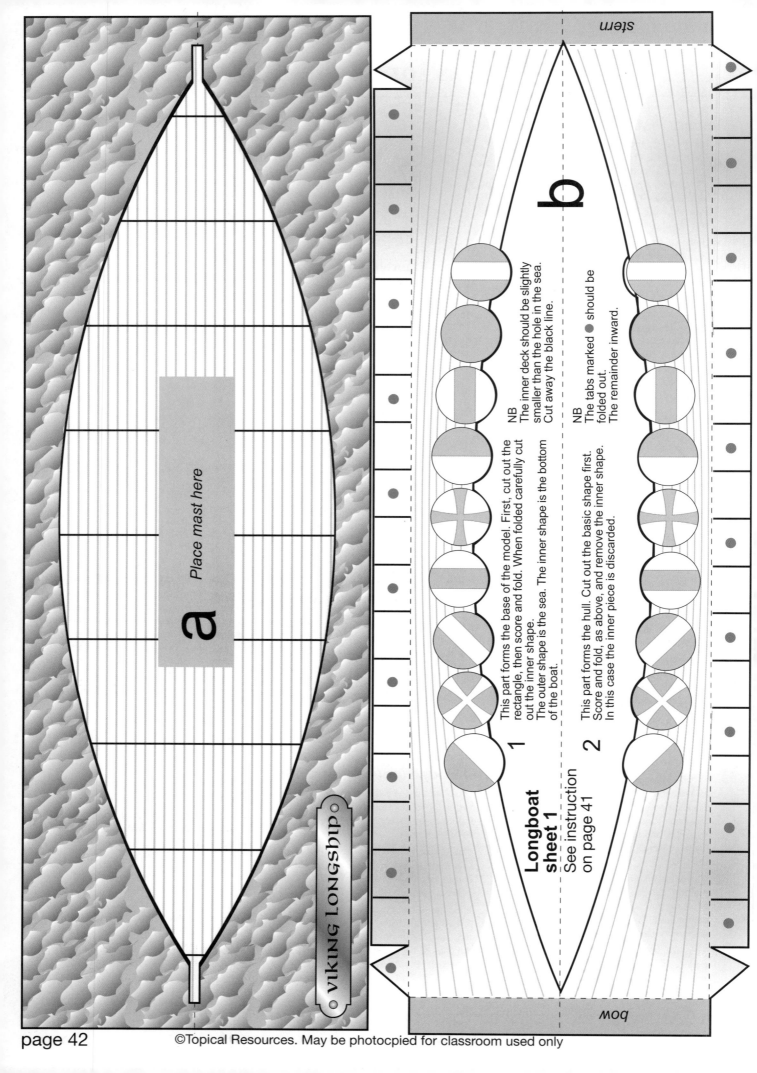

a

*Place mast here*

b

stern

bow

**NB**
The inner deck should be slightly smaller than the hole in the sea. Cut away the black line.

1  This part forms the base of the model. First, cut out the rectangle, then score and fold. When folded carefully cut out the inner shape. The outer shape is the sea. The inner shape is the bottom of the boat.

**NB**
The tabs marked ● should be folded out. The remainder inward.

2  This part forms the hull. Cut out the basic shape first. Score and fold, as above, and remove the inner shape. In this case the inner piece is discarded.

**Longboat sheet 1**
See instruction on page 41

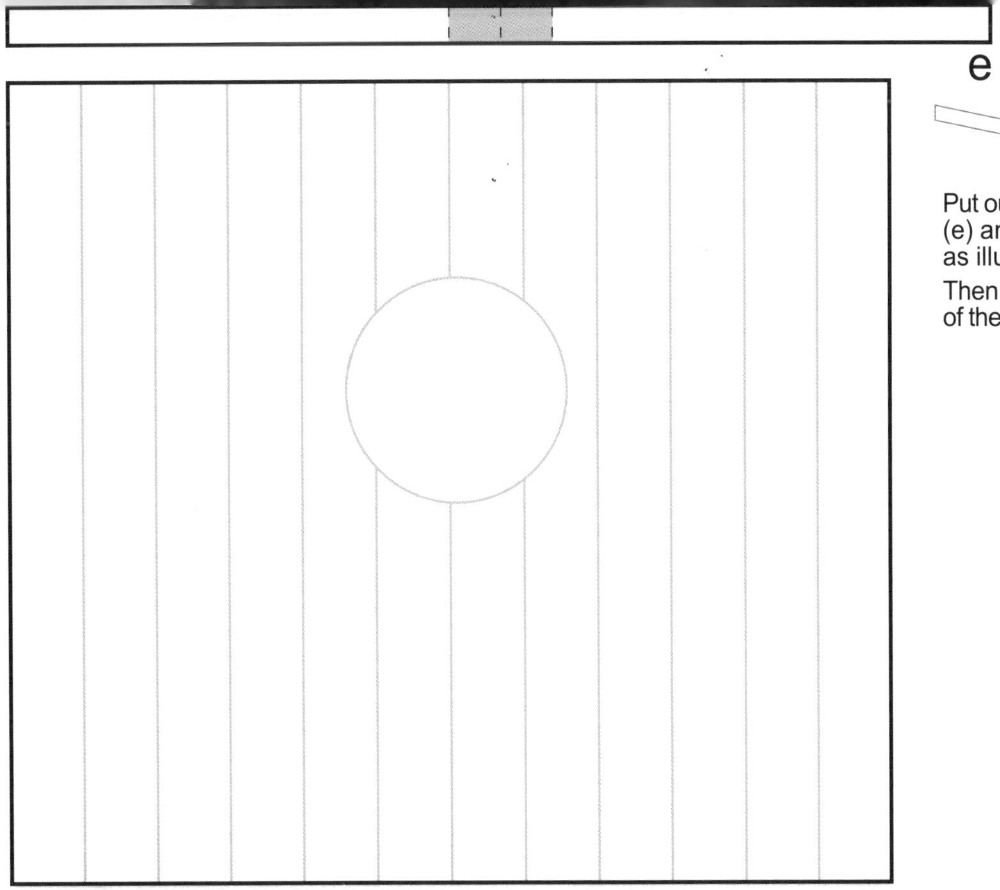

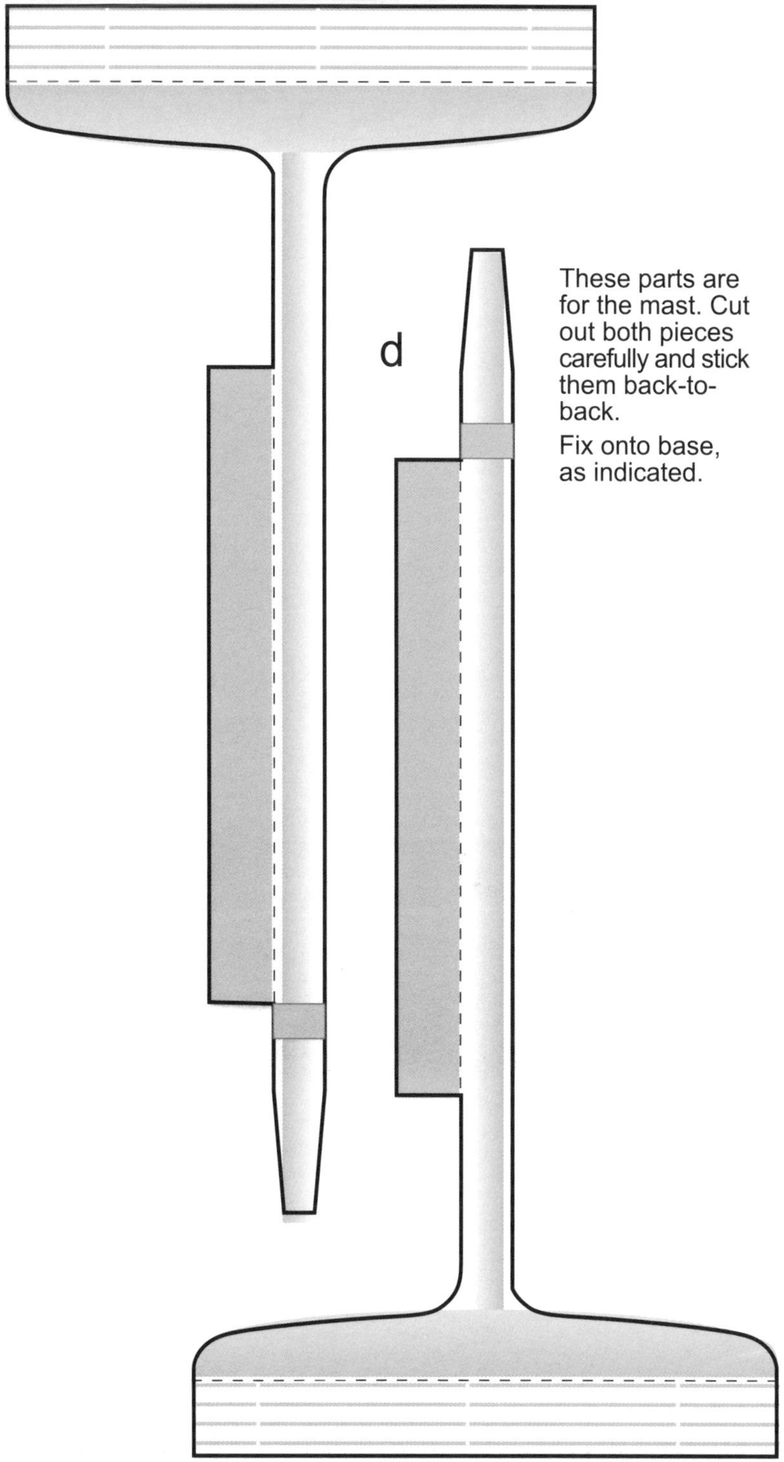

These parts are for the mast. Cut out both pieces carefully and stick them back-to-back.
Fix onto base, as indicated.

d

e

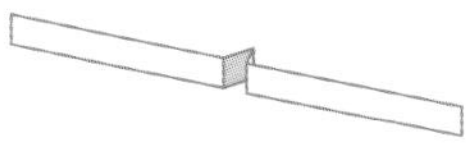

Put out and fold part (e) and fix to mast as illustrated.
Then fix to the back of the top of the sail.

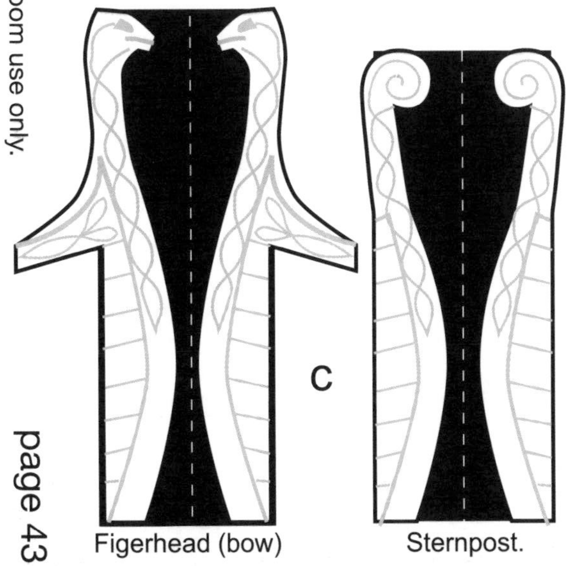

**Longboat sheet 2**

See instruction on page 41

Cut out parts (c).
Score and fold.
Fix to bow and stern of the hull, and allow to dry fully.
When dry cut away the black area.

Sternpost.

c

Figerhead (bow)

# Viking House sheet 1

See instruction on page 41

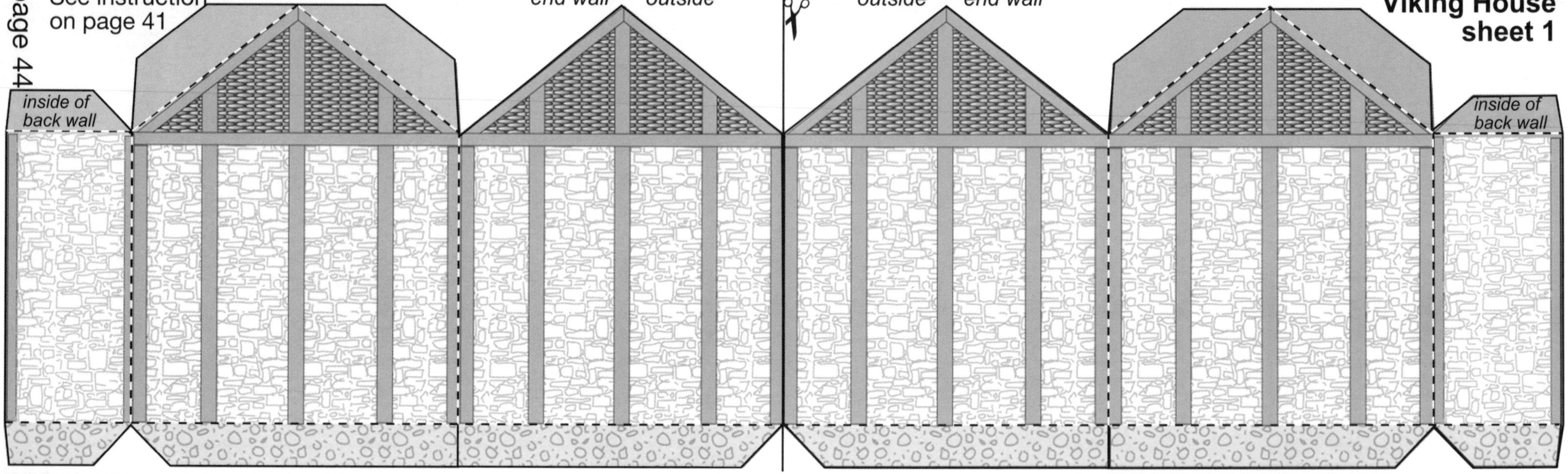
inside of back wall
end wall
outside
outside
end wall
inside of back wall

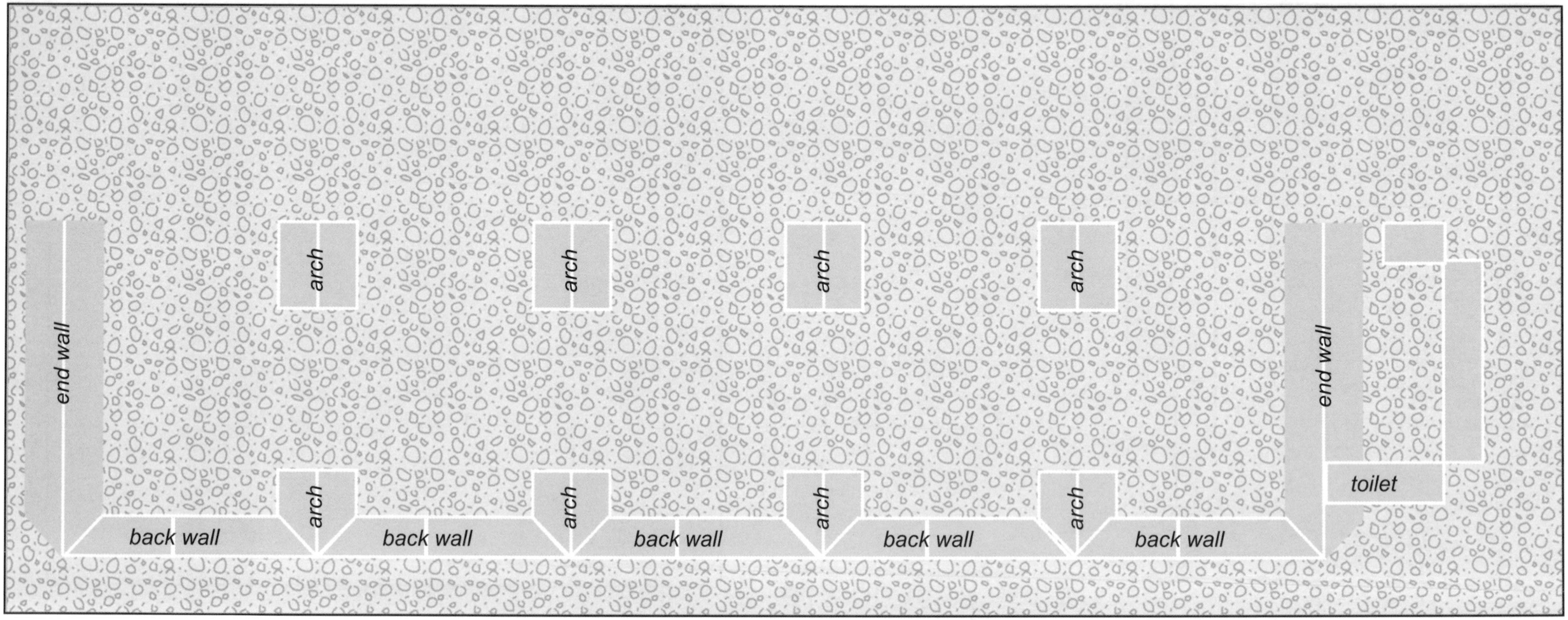
end wall
arch
arch
arch
arch
end wall
toilet
arch
arch
arch
arch
back wall
back wall
back wall
back wall
back wall

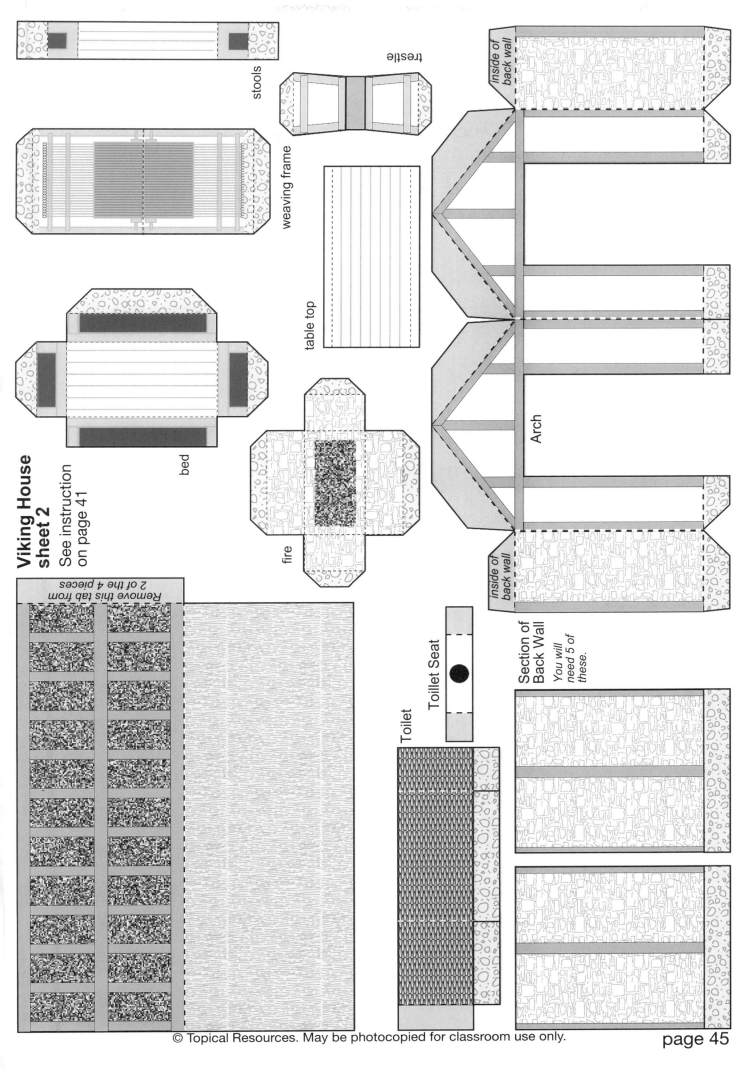

**Viking House sheet 2**

See instruction on page 41

stools

trestle

weaving frame

table top

bed

fire

inside of back wall

inside of back wall

Arch

Remove this tab from 2 of the 4 pieces

Section of Back Wall

*You will need 5 of these.*

Toilet

Toillet Seat

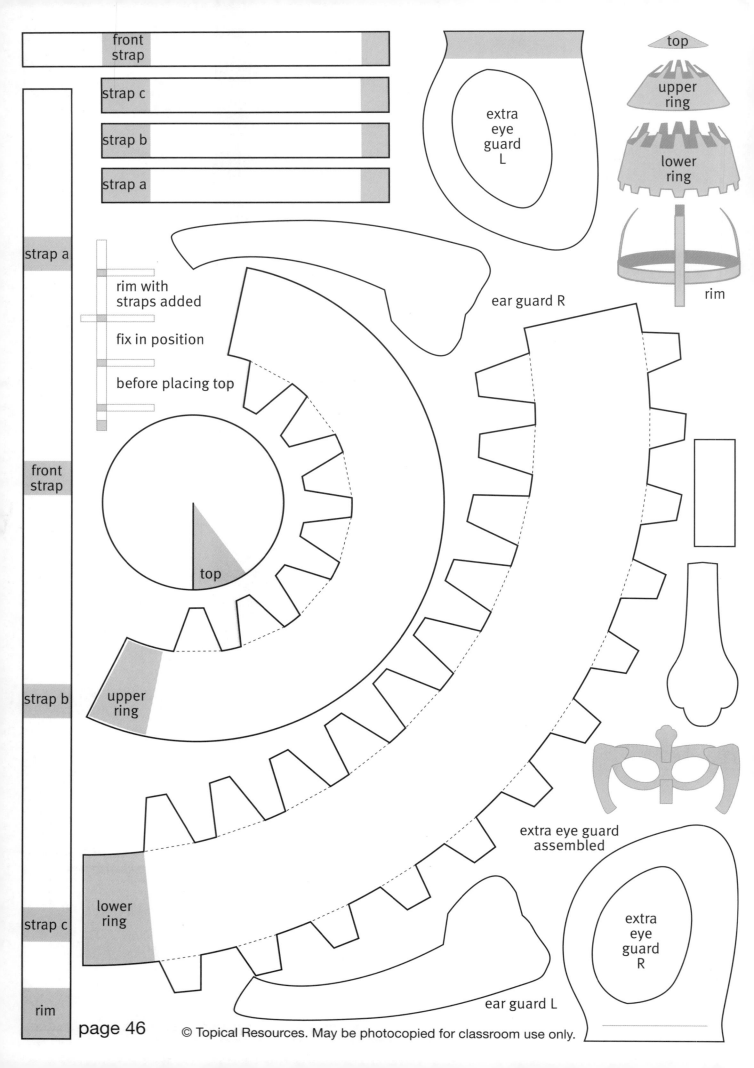

front strap

strap c

strap b

strap a

strap a

front strap

strap b

strap c

rim

rim with straps added

fix in position

before placing top

top

upper ring

lower ring

extra eye guard L

ear guard R

top

upper ring

lower ring

rim

extra eye guard assembled

extra eye guard R

ear guard L

page 46

© Topical Resources. May be photocopied for classroom use only.

# Viking Longboat Figurehead

See instruction on page 41

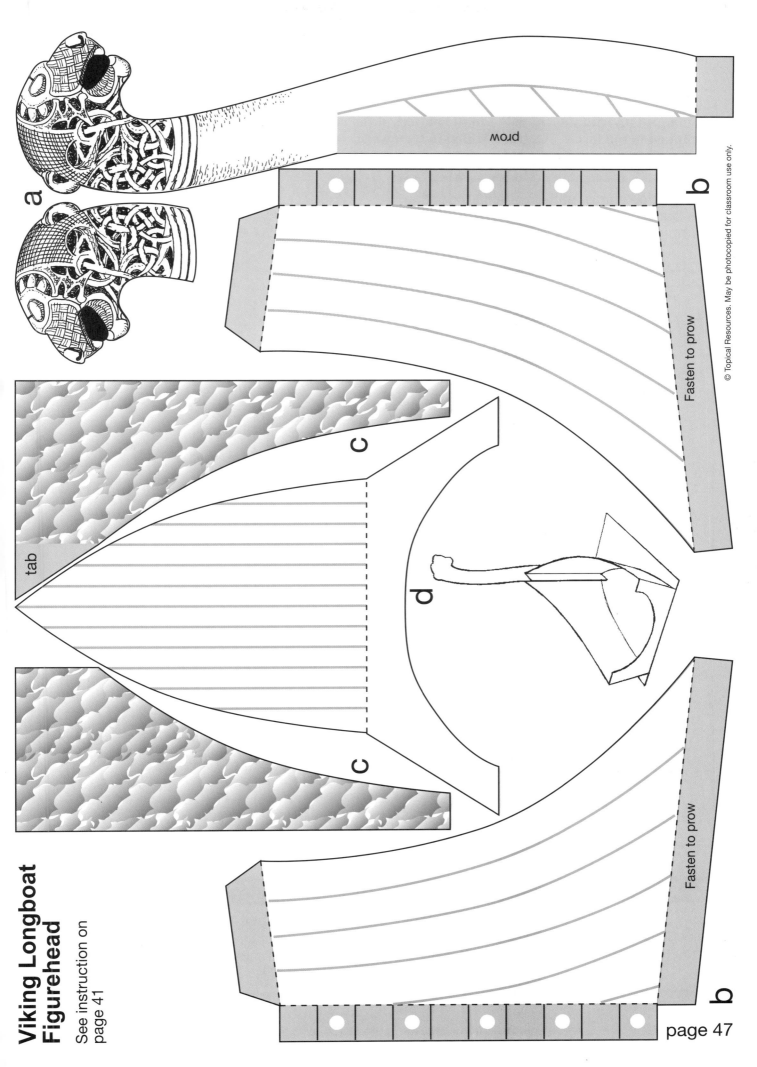

prow

b

Fasten to prow

tab

c

c

d

Fasten to prow

b

page 47

# Viking Spiral Decoration

The Vikings used spiral interlocking patterns to show that they believed that their lives were interwoven and mingled up with the animals and the powers of the natural world. They believed that their destiny was linked to the forces of nature, which in turn were controlled by their Viking Gods.

## Task A

In the three animal patterns below, continue the patterns, drawing over the faint lines to complete the designs.

## Task B

Now colour your patterns carefully. Use the Vikings favourite colours; red, blue, green and yellow.

## Task C

Search for other Viking Spiral Patterns in reference books and make your own collection of this form of Viking art.

# Using I.C.T. for your Viking Topic

## Task 1: How to find and print a Viking wood carving from Microsoft Encarta Encyclopedia

Check that **Microsoft Encarta Encyclopedia** is on your screen.

1   In the **'FIND'** box at the top left hand side of your screen type the words *'Viking Wood Carvings'* press the return key or click with your mouse. Text and a picture of a Viking Wood Carving will appear on your screen.

2   To print this picture :

3   Click on **Options** at the top of the screen.

4   Click on **Print** in the options menu.

5   Check that the image circle has a black dot in it. If it has not, click in the circle so that one appears.

6   Check that the printer is switched on, then click on **Print** at the bottom of the box.

7   Collect your information from the printer.

8   Using the text information, carefully write a title for your printed picture. Now neatly add several sentences about the Viking carving that you have researched from the text, so that your work can be added to a class display on the Vikings.

## Task 2: How to find and print a portrait of Eric the Red from Microsoft Encarta Encyclopedia

Check that **Microsoft Encarta Encyclopedia** is on your screen.

1   In the **'FIND'** box at the top left hand side of your screen type the words *'Eric the Red'* press the return key or click with your mouse. Text and a picture of Eric the Red will appear on your screen.

2   To print this picture :

3   Click on **Options** at the top of the screen.

4   Click on **Print** in the options menu.

5   Check that the image circle has a black dot in it. If it has not, click in the circle so that one appears.

6   Check that the printer is switched on, then click on **Print** at the bottom of the box.

7   Collect your information from the printer.

8   Using the text information, carefully write a title for your printed picture. Now neatly add several sentences about Eric the Red's life that you have researched from the text, so that your work can be added to a class display on the Vikings.

## Task 3: Taking it Further

Using a similar method as outlined above research for yourself the voyages of other Viking explorers or Viking ships so that you can add this research to your Viking display.

# A Real Viking 'Whodunit'

**The Vikings sailed up rivers to find easy targets for their raids.**

### Task: Consider the facts

Read the information on this page, considering a typical Viking raid. Discuss why the Vikings buried their treasure box. Now study the facts about the Cuerdale Hoard on page 51. Finally, tackle the task on Page 51.

### The Facts

- Viking longboats were able to sail a long way up rivers because their ships were very shallow.
- They attacked towns and villages a long way from the sea.
- The Saxon people felt safe from attack by sea raiders, because they were a long way from the sea.

### Before a Viking Raid

- Vikings sailed near the place they wanted to attack at night.
- The Viking leader told his men to dig a hole on the river bank.
- Next they put their treasure box in the hole.
- Then they put the earth over it again.
- The Vikings thought that the treasure was safe.
- The Vikings would hide their boat in bushes or reeds.

### The Raid

- The Vikings attacked at dawn.
- The Saxon people were asleep in their beds.
- The Saxons did not have their weapons close to them.
- The Vikings attack was a surprise to the Saxons.
- The Vikings killed anybody who tried to fight them.
- The Vikings took away gold, silver, jewels and money.
- Sometimes they took Saxons to be their slaves.
- The Vikings often set fire to the houses

### After a Viking Raid

- The Vikings dug up their treasure chest.
- The Vikings lit a big fire.
- One of the Vikings who was clever with metal, melted down any silver or gold object that they had stolen.
- He made a mould in the sand by the river. Then he poured the hot metal in to the mould.
- When it was cool, he put the metal in the treasure chest. Any coins were put in the treasure chest too.
- The Vikings sailed away.

# The Evidence of the Cuerdale Hoard

## Found !

In May 1840 some workmen working on the banks of the river Ribble at Cuerdale near Preston Lancs., dug up a large decaying wooden chest, bound with bands of iron and lined with lead.

## Contents !

Spilling out from the chest came:

- Rings, armlets, chains and many jewellery items.
- Silver ingots weighing over 25 kilogrammes.
- 10,000 coins, both Saxon and Viking, from all all over the Viking world.

**The Cuerdale Hoard**
Many of these items can still be seen at the British Museum in London
© Copyright The British Museum

### Your Task: Using the Evidence

A Read the two pages about the Viking 'Whodunit'. Discuss with your group or partner how you think the treasure might have come to be buried in the banks of the River Ribble.

B Now consider each of the following possibilities. Think carefully about why the treasure was left in the river bank, and not collected by the people who hid it there.

1 Vikings raiding Preston, a Saxon town, hid their treasure before the raid.

2 The treasure was hidden by the Saxon people of Preston, as they heard of Viking raiders coming to their town.

3 A rich landowner living in a hall near Preston, buried his treasure so that no one could steal it from him.

4 A thief had stolen a rich man's goods, and hid them to collect later.

C Finally, after careful thought, present your solution to the Viking 'Whodunit' to your classmates. You may wish to write out your case. Be prepared to answer questions from your classmates about your particular solution.

# Viking Game for Two Players - Hneftefafl

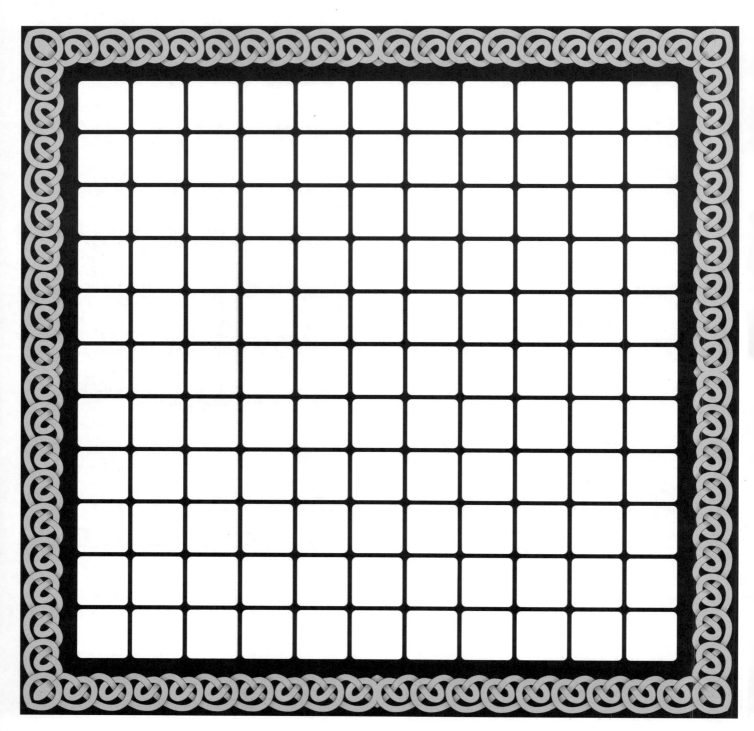

The Vikings made up this game because a large part of their lives was spent defending their tribe and their Chief, or raiding another tribe and its Chief. Vikings showed cunning, careful planning, and thought about their next move in war. You will have to show these Viking qualities if you want to win.

# Viking Game for Two Players - Hneftefafl

*The Dragons*

*The King's men*

*Cut out all the pieces*

**The King**

*This shows how the pieces are laid out to begin the game.*

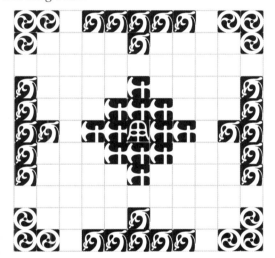

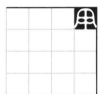

*The King wins if he gets to any of the 4 corners of the board.*

*The King loses if he is surrounded on 4 sides by his opponents.*

## How to set up the game

The 24 dragon pieces are put on 6 squares at each side of the board. The King is placed in the centre, surrounded by his 12 axe men, and his 12 shields are placed in the corners of the board. See the example.

Decide who is the King, and who is to play the Dragons. The Dragons move first.

## The aim of the game

The aim of the King is to get to one of the 4 corners of the board. The aim of the Dragons is to surround the King, on all four sides. The winner is the player who achieves his/her aim first.

## Moving your pieces

The King can only move one square at a time, left, right, up or down, but not diagonally. He cannot jump over another piece.

All the other pieces can also move left, right, up or down (not diagonally), but they can move as many squares in one direction as possible. They too cannot jump over other pieces.

To capture, take or remove an opponents piece, it must be surrounded on both sides by two pieces, either horizontally, vertically or diagonally. See the diagram across.

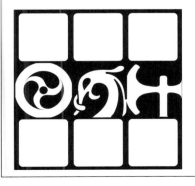  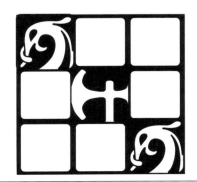

*In each of these three examples the piece in the middle is taken.*

# Make a Viking Brooch

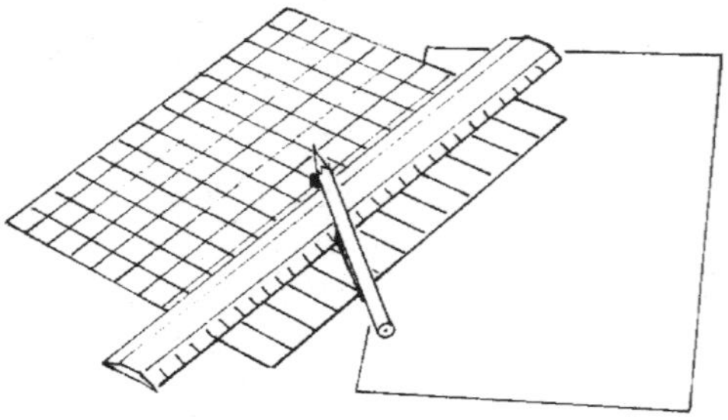

**1**

Using ruler and pencil, divide different coloured pieces of paper into 1cm. squares. You will have to decide how many different colours you want to use in your broach.

**2**

------------------------------------------------
------------------------------------------------
------------------------------------------------
------------------------------------------------

**3**

Research in reference books to find examples of Viking Cloak Brooches. Practice a few different designs on a scrap piece of paper or a sketch pad. Remember that most Viking Brooches were circular or oval in shape.

**4**

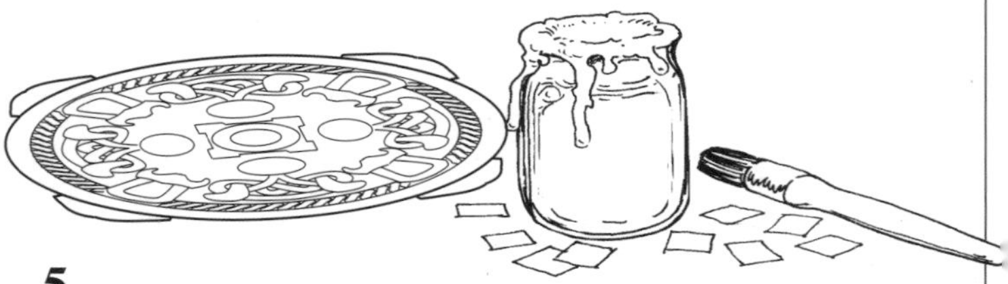

------------------------------------------------
------------------------------------------------
------------------------------------------------
------------------------------------------------

**5**

Now, carefully paste the coloured squares onto the correct places on your brooch design. Work steadily until your design is all covered.

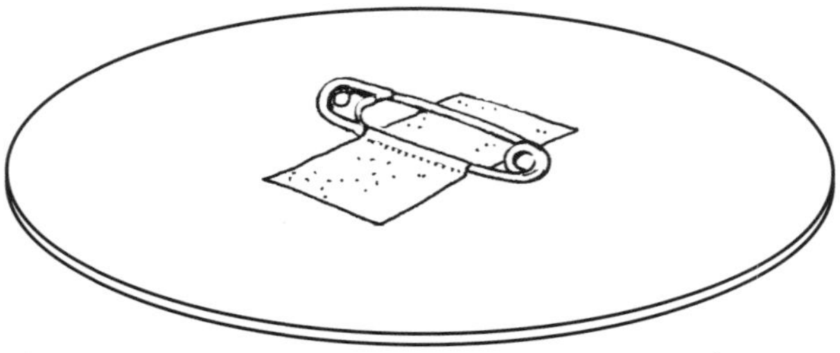

**6**

------------------------------------------------
------------------------------------------------
------------------------------------------------
------------------------------------------------

## Task A

Carefully study the pictures and text about how to make a Viking Brooch. Write your own simple instructions to fill in the missing spaces.

## Task B

Now follow your instructions to make your own Viking Brooch. The designs below may help you.

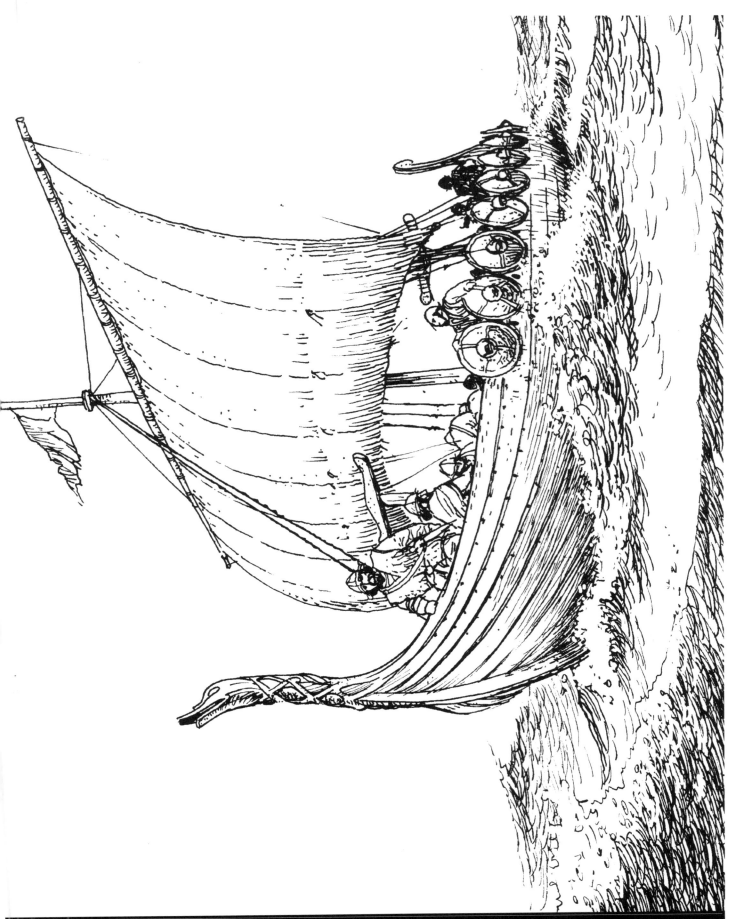

# Paint your own Viking Voyager's Picture

Research in reference books to find the correct colours when you paint this picture of Viking Voyagers a sea.

# Viking Trading Towns

The Vikings were clever at making things out of metal, wood and rich stones.

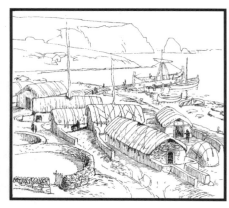

The towns were beside rivers or by the sea, so that the Vikings could bring goods from many lands in their ships.

The Vikings would change the goods they had made for other goods that they wanted.

The towns had many different craftsmen. They worked in the open front of their houses, right on the street.

The towns had a wooden fence around them to protect the craftsmen and traders from raids by other Vikings.

People from all over the Viking world brought rich goods to sell in the trading towns like York, London and Dublin.

---

1    The Vikings were clever at _ _ _ _ _ _ things out of _ _ _ _ _ , wood and stones.

2    The towns were _ _ _ _ _ _ rivers or by the _ _ _ , so that the Vikings could bring _ _ _ _ _ from many lands in their ships.

3    The _ _ _ _ _ _ _ would change the goods they had _ _ _ _ for other goods that they _ _ _ _ _ _ .

4    The towns had many different _ _ _ _ _ _ _ _ _ . They worked in the open _ _ _ _ _ of their houses, right on the _ _ _ _ _ _ .

5    The towns had a wooden _ _ _ _ _ around them to _ _ _ _ _ _ _ the craftsmen and traders from raids by other _ _ _ _ _ _ _ .

6    People from all over the Viking _ _ _ _ _ brought rich _ _ _ _ _ to sell in the trading towns like _ _ _ _ .

7    Carefully draw and colour your own picture of a Viking craftsman at work in his house.

# Viking Trading Towns.

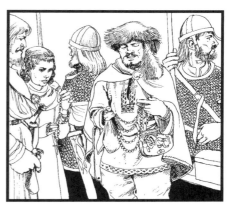

The Vikings were very clever at making things out of metal, wood and precious stones. They would trade these in the markets of trading towns. These towns were built close to rivers and the sea, so that the Vikings could bring their goods from many lands to the market in their ships. The Vikings would change the things that they had made for things they wanted. This was called bartering.

Soon the towns had many craftsmen making and trading goods. Each craftsman would work in the open front of his house right on the street, so that people coming to the town would see what he was making. The houses would be made of wood and mud and the streets were made of wooden planks to make it easy for people to move about the town.

The Viking trading towns would have a high fence on top of a mound of earth all around them with fortified gates, to guard against raiders. The trading towns would have wooden jetties sticking out into the river or sea so that ships could tie up close to the trading streets and unload their good easily. People from all over the Viking world would bring goods to Viking trading towns like York, London and Dublin to buy and sell. The Vikings name for York was Yorvik. It traded as a Viking market from 833 till 1070 when it was destroyed by Norman invaders led by William the Conqueror.

**A**

1 Where did the Vikings build their Trading towns?

2 What did Vikings call the changing of one thing they had made for something else they wanted?

3 Why did the Vikings traders have the front of their houses open?

4 Why did the Vikings have jetties jutting out into the rivers or the sea near their towns?

5 When was Yorvik a Viking trading town?

**B**

1 Why do you think the Viking trading towns had a mound and fence all around them?

2 Why do you think that people from all over the Viking world visited Yorvik?

**C** Carefully draw and colour your own picture of ships tied up to a jetty at a Viking trading town.

# Viking Trading Towns

The Vikings were skilled craftsmen, they made many fine articles out of metal, leather, wood, glass or precious stones. They would trade the articles they had made for things they themselves wanted in towns specialising in trade. The towns where these markets were held were situated beside rivers or by the sea. This meant that Vikings could have easy access to the trading town in their boats and ships. The process of changing one article for others was called bartering.

The trading towns had jetties jutting out into the river or sea so that the Viking ships could moor up close to the place where they were going to trade. The whole town was surrounded by a large mound of earth on top of which was a high fence to protect the traders from raids by Viking pirates. Streets of wooden planks lined with open fronted wooden and mud houses, with larger wooden buildings used as warehouses, would make up the towns.

The craftsmen and women would work in the open front of their homes so that visiting traders could see the goods they were making and easily purchase them. Traders from all over the Viking world would bring a vast variety of goods and materials to barter or sell in the towns of Viking Britain. The towns like York, Exeter, London and Dublin soon came to make their own money from silver and gold. Coins minted in these places have been found by archaeologists digging up the trading town sites.

The most famous British Viking trading town, Yorvik (York), has the ruins of many streets of Viking traders homes and craft workshops. Archaeologists have discovered the remains of many craft shops with many wonderful craft items as well as the remains of clothing, food and household utensils. All these artefacts have enabled the archaeologists to state that Yorvik had trading visitors from Russia, Turkey, Italy, Spain and Iraq as well as giving us details of the daily life of the craft workers of the town.

## A

1  What materials did the Viking Craftsmen use to make their goods?

2  Why did the Vikings build their trading towns near rivers or by the sea?

3  Where were there Viking trading towns in Britain?

4  How did the Vikings take part in bartering?

5  What was the reason for having wooden jetties sticking out into the water in Viking trading towns?

6  How do we know all about the trading town of Yorvik?

7  Why did the Viking traders have open fronted shops and houses?

8  What do you think was made in the mint at Yorvik.

## B

1  What evidence tells you that Viking trading towns were sometimes raided by Viking pirates?

2  Why do you think that Viking traders came to York?

3  How do you think we know that Vikings from Russia visited Yorvik?

4  What evidence tells us that there were Viking mints in Yorvik, Exeter, London and Dublin?

5  Why do you think that we know a great deal about the daily life of a Viking craftsman in Yorvik?

**C**  Carefully draw and colour your own picture of Viking Traders bartering their goods in a trading town.

# Viking Trading Towns

The Vikings had many skilled craftsmen who worked in metals, wood and precious stones producing many wonderful items, which they traded with other people in market towns throughout the Viking world. In the old Viking lands which are now Denmark, Sweden and Norway, these market or trading towns were built on river banks or close to the sea, such as the towns of Hedeby, Gothenburg and Birka. This was done so that goods could be transported easily from all parts of the Viking world by ship. Jetties would jut out into the river or sea so that the ships could easily unload their cargoes.

The trading towns were surrounded by a raised bank of earth, which was surmounted by a high wooden fence as a defence from other Viking raiders. When the Vikings settled in Britain they built trading towns at York, Exeter, Dublin and London. The settlement at York was named Yorvik by the Vikings who used it as a trading town from 833 until its burning in 1070 by William the Conqueror, the Norman descendant of Vikings who had invaded northern France.

The Viking trading towns had streets of wooden planks, lined by wooden and mud houses, running inland from the sea or river on which these towns were set. Many of the houses would have open fronts where the craftsmen would carry on their skilled crafts in full view of passing customers. Their homes therefore had a triple purpose being workshops, homes and shops. At first many of the people trading in these towns would exchange their goods for other goods in a system called 'bartering'. Later York, London, Exeter and Dublin would all have their own Viking Mint where coins of gold and silver were made or minted and used as payment for goods.

Archaeologists have discovered Viking age coins from Russia, Iraq, Italy and Spain in their excavations of Yorvik, London, Exeter and Dublin, showing that traders were coming to York from all parts of Europe as well as from parts of Asia. Archaeological 'digs' have shown that craftsmen producing articles in horn, antler, silver, gold, copper, wood, clay, leather, glass and precious stones were working in Viking York and were serving customers from all over the Viking world. Further evidence points to a brisk trade in food, clothing and human slaves in these British Viking trading towns. All these towns must have been busy bustling places of trade serving Britain and the Viking world with a huge range of products.

**A**

1   Why do you think that the Vikings built their towns near rivers or coasts?

2   Why do you think that the Viking trading towns were surrounded by a raised bank and fence ?

3   Why do you think the Viking towns had wooden planked streets?

4   What do you understand by the word 'bartering'?

5   What do you think is made in a mint?

6   Why did Viking traders have open fronted houses?

7   How can you tell that York was a very busy Viking Trading post?

8   Where were the main Viking Trading towns in Europe?

**B**

1   Define the words : craftsmen, archaeologist, customers.

2   What evidence tells you that Viking York produced items of jewellery ?

3   What do you understand by 'bustling' places of trade?

4   What evidence tells you that some traders came to Viking York from Asia?

**C**   Use reference books to research:

1   The types of ships used by Viking traders .

2   The coins that Vikings used for trade in Britain.

# The Vikings and Alfred the Saxon

In 871 the Vikings sailed up the River Thames to raid the towns in Alfred's kingdom.

In 876 the Vikings raided on horseback. They burnt towns in Alfred's land, Wessex.

Alfred did not fight the Vikings. He gives them money to go away from his land.

When the Vikings came again in 878, Alfred fought them. The Vikings won and Alfred had to hide.

A woman let Alfred stay in her home. She told Alfred to watch the cakes cooking. Alfred let them burn.

Alfred and his men won a battle against the Vikings. The Vikings said they would never fight Alfred again.

1   In 871 the _ _ _ _ _ _ _  sailed up the River Thames to _ _ _ _  towns in Alfred's Kingdom.

2   In 876 the Vikings _ _ _ _ _ _  on horseback. They _ _ _ _ _ _ towns in _ _ _ _ _ _ _  land.

3   Alfred did not _ _ _ _ _  the Vikings. He gave them _ _ _ _ _ to go _ _ _ _.

4   When the _ _ _ _ _ _ _ came in 878, Alfred _ _ _ _ _ _ them. Alfred had to _ _ _ _ .

5   A woman told Alfred to _ _ _ _ _ her cakes _ _ _ _ _ _ _ _ . Alfred  _ _ _ the cakes burn.

6   Alfred and his _ _ _ won a battle against the _ _ _ _ _ _ _ . The Vikings said they would never fight _ _ _ _ _ _  again.

7   Carefully  draw your own picture of the Vikings fighting with Alfred.

# The Vikings and Alfred the Saxon

Alfred became King of Wessex in the south of Britain in 866. In 871 the Vikings sailed their ships up the River Thames and attacked towns and villages in Alfred's kingdom, Wessex.

In 876 the Vikings raided Wessex on horseback. They burnt towns and villages. Alfred did not fight the Vikings, instead he gave them money to go away from his land.

When the Vikings came back to raid his land in 877, Alfred and his army fought the Vikings. The Vikings won and Alfred and his men had to hide from the Vikings in the forests and marshy lands.

One day, when he was hiding from the Vikings, Alfred asked a poor woman if he could rest in her house. She let Alfred rest but she asked him to watch her cakes cooking on the fire. She went out and Alfred did not watch the cakes. When she came back the cakes were burnt, so she beat Alfred with her spoon.

When the Vikings came back to raid Wessex in 878 Alfred and his army beat them in battle. He told the Vikings they could live in the east of England but they must not to raid Alfred's kingdom ever again.

**A**

1 When did Alfred become king of Wessex?
2 Which river did the Vikings sail up in 871?
3 What did the Vikings do to the towns and villages of Wessex in 871?
4 How did the Vikings travel to Wessex in 876?
5 What happened when the Vikings and Alfred fought in 877?
6 What did Alfred tell the Vikings in 878?

**B**

1 Why do you think that Alfred gave the Vikings money in 876?
2 Why do you think the woman beat Alfred with her spoon?

**C** Carefully draw and colour your own picture of the Vikings raiding a town in Wessex.

# The Vikings and Alfred the Saxon

Alfred became the Saxon King of Wessex in south western England in 866. He had heard that other Saxon kingdoms in Britain had been raided by the fierce fighting Vikings from across the seas. He was surprised when the Vikings sailed up the River Thames to attack towns and villages in his kingdom in 871. The Vikings took jewellery, money and people away with them. They used the people as slaves.

For the next four years Viking raiders sailed along the coasts and up the rivers of Wessex, raiding Alfred's kingdom. The people of Wessex wanted Alfred to rid them of the Viking raids. So when the Vikings raided Wessex on horseback in 876, Alfred met the Viking leader Guthrum and gave him money and treasures to leave the people of Wessex alone.

In 877 Guthrum and his Vikings attacked Wessex again. This time Alfred and the Saxon people of Wessex decided to fight with the Vikings. Guthrum and the Vikings beat Alfred and the Saxons in battle. Alfred and his army had to flee into the marshy places of his kingdom. They had to hide from the Vikings who were chasing them. One day Alfred asked a poor woman if he could rest in her house. The woman let Alfred rest whilst she went to get some water, but she told Alfred to watch her cakes cooking on the fire. When she returned the cakes were burnt so she beat Alfred with her spoon.

In 878 Guthrum and his Vikings again raided Wessex. Alfred sent out messengers to all his people to join him secretly near Chippenham to attack the Vikings there. Alfred and his army beat the Vikings and killed many of them. Guthrum realised he was beaten and agreed with Alfred to leave Wessex alone. Alfred let the Vikings live in the eastern part of England, which became known as Danelaw. Wessex remained a Saxon kingdom.

**A**

1 Where was Alfred the Saxon's kingdom of Wessex ?

2 Why was Alfred surprised in 871?

3 What did the Vikings take when they raided towns and villages?

4 When did the Vikings raid Wessex on horse back?

5 Why did Alfred give Guthrum money and treasure in 876 ?

6 Why did Alfred and his men have to hide in 877?

7 How did Alfred arrange for his people to meet at Chippenham in 878?

**B**

1 What evidence tells you that Alfred and his men were afraid of the Vikings?

2 What evidence tells you that Wessex was a rich kingdom?

3 Why do you think the woman was angry with Alfred ?

4 Why do you think Alfred let the cakes burn?

5 Why do you think Guthrum was happy to make peace with Alfred and the Saxons in 878?

**C** Carefully draw and colour your own picture of Guthrum the Viking and Alfred the Saxon making peace in 878.

# The Vikings and King Alfred the Saxon.

In 866 Alfred became King of Wessex, an area of south western England. He had heard that the Saxon kingdom of Anglia had been raided by Vikings, fierce fighting men from Norway and Denmark. He was surprised in the summer of 871 when some Viking raiders sailed up the River Thames and attacked towns and villages of Wessex. His people had many of their finest jewels and treasures stolen by the Vikings, who took many of the Saxon people of Wessex away with them to be slaves. In the following four years the Vikings attacked the towns and villages along the coasts of Alfred's kingdom, Wessex. These raids frightened the people of Wessex, who wanted their King to rid them of the threat of the Vikings. So when the Vikings who were now living in Anglia attacked Alfred's kingdom on horseback in 876, Alfred met the Viking leader Guthrum and gave him money and treasure to leave Wessex alone.

But the next year, 877, Guthrum and his Vikings attacked Wessex by land and by sea. Alfred and his Saxon army fought against the Vikings but they were beaten in battle. Alfred and some of his warriors continued to raid the Vikings who had settled into the Saxon towns in Wessex, but the Vikings easily beat them off. Alfred and his men had to retreat into the island of Athelney, a hilly area in the middle of marshes and bogs in the west of Wessex. The Vikings pursued Alfred forcing him to run away and hide. One day when he was hiding from the Vikings in a poor woman's hut, Alfred was told by the woman to watch her cakes cooking on the fire whilst she went to bring some water. When she got back her cakes were burnt and the woman beat Alfred with her spoon, as she did not know that the stranger in her house was her king.

In 878 when the Guthrum and his Vikings returned to raid Wessex, Alfred sent out secret messengers to tell his warriors to meet him secretly near Chippenham ready to fight the Vikings. The Saxon warriors were glad to see their king ready to fight the raiders. Alfred and his army stole up on the Vikings in their camp, and in the fight that followed many Viking warriors were killed. Guthrum was forced to surrender. The Vikings realising that they were beaten agreed to leave Wessex alone. Alfred and Guthrum divided England up into a Western part for the Saxons and an Eastern part for the Vikings. The Viking part became known as Danelaw, as Guthrum's Vikings came from Denmark. Guthrum and many of his Viking raiders were made Christians like Alfred and his Saxons. In this way Alfred and Guthrum brought peace between the people of England and the Viking raiders.

## A

1 Why do you think Alfred was surprised in the summer of 871?

2 What do you think happened when Viking warriors attacked a Saxon village?

3 Why do you think the Vikings raided the towns and villages of Wessex?

4 What caused Alfred and his warriors to retreat to Athelney?

5 Why do you think the poor woman did not recognise Alfred as her King ?

6 Why do you think that Alfred let the cakes burn?

7 What is a retreat?

8 Why do you think Alfred sent out secret messengers to call his army together?

## B

1 Define the words: pursued and surrender.

2 What evidence tells you that the Vikings were fierce warriors?

3 What do you think made Guthrum and Alfred divide England into two parts?

4 Why do you think that Alfred made the Vikings and Guthrum become christians?

## C

1 Use reference books to research where the main Saxon towns in Wessex were situated.

2 Viking raids on the monasteries of England.

# Time to Spare Activities

1 Write a letter from Leif Eriksson to his family in Greenland about his voyage westwards.

2 Write the diary of a Viking Trader in Yorvik in the winter of 950.

3 Make a model of the Norse God Thor.

4 Make a Viking Trader's house and shop in a shoebox.

5 Design and make a Viking shield.

6 Draw a picture of shops in a Viking British town.

7 Research all you can about Viking Trading ships.

8 Write the diary of a Viking Lord for three days as he raids a British monastery.

9 Design your own badge for the sail of a Viking Longboat.

10 Find out the names of people and places near to you that come to us from Viking times.

11 Draw the treasure that a Viking raider might plunder from a raid on a British town.

12 Design and make a Viking cloak broach.

13 Research as much as you can about King Knut (some books call him Canute).

16 Research the history of a Viking town or village near to you.

14 Design your own Viking belt buckle.

15 Make a poster of all the different types of Viking boats.

17 List the equipment the Vikings used for cooking and compare it with a modern kitchen.

18 Write a Biography of Eric the Red.

19 Make a poster advertising a Viking New Year feast.

20 Make your own booklet of Viking jewellery designs.

21 Research as much as you can about the games Viking children played.

22 Design your own Viking gravestone.

23 Make a model of a Viking Battle Axe.

24 Choose a year in Viking times and find out as much as you can about that year.

25 Make your own booklet up about Viking women.

26 Make your own poster of Viking clothes.

27 Make a poster of Viking age coins.

28 Make your own booklet of Viking weapons.

29 Make your own map of places in Europe that the Vikings sailed to.

30 Write and illustrate your own Viking saga.

31 Write out a list of Viking kings or leaders with their nicknames.

32 Research all you can about Harald Hardrada.